ANI

Hidden

Published by Blue Door Press

Cover Design: Alex Kirby

ISBN: 978 - 1916475489

For my parents, Vera & John

Written on the body is a secret code only visible in certain lights: the accumulation of a lifetime gather there.

Jeanette Winterson, *Written On The Body*

ONE

1

I am dancing, my legs, hips and arms tracing patterns through dark smoke-filled air. Other people's bodies are pressed close to mine. I watch our shadows moving against the wall. The music reverberates against my bones, echoes inside my body. A strobe washes my chest bright white and the gold sequins on my neckline sparkle.

We're in the basement of a bar on Charlotte Street, at a birthday party for someone I've never met. I've come with my friends Ioana and Kwong.

Ioana, almost six foot in her heels, moves over to me and puts her mouth close to my ear. 'Having a good time?'

I nod and smile. 'And you?'

'Not bad. Anyone you like the look of?'

'I saw one cute guy. But I think he's with someone.'

We're early thirties and single.

We leave the party just after midnight.

'So, what's next, you two?' Kwong asks as we stand on the pavement, the mild April night a relief after the smoky basement.

'How about a lift home?' says Ioana.

'I'm starving. Come for falafel. Then I'll drop you both off.'

We drive through town, cutting across Great Portland Street, Harley Street and Baker Street, until we reach Edgware Road. It's

3

late but lots of places are still open. Lebanese music drifts out of cafes and the open windows of cars. Groups of men sit at pavement tables, smoking hookahs and drinking tea.

Kwong takes us to his favourite place. On the counter, a huge lump of doner gyrates slowly round a steel spike and the waiter winks at Ioana and me. I look at our reflections in the mirror behind him. Her blonde head a few inches above my darker one. We've always envied each other's hair. She wanted my thick waves and I the fine straight lengths, which always fell so effortlessly into place.

At a white, brightly lit Formica table we eat falafel wrapped in pitta and pass round an apple-scented hookah. Ioana and I tease Kwong about a girl in a pink top he tried, unsuccessfully, to chat up at the party.

It's almost two when they drop me in South Hampstead before heading on to Notting Hill. All the lights in my building are out and the dark glass of the windows stares blankly at me. Inside, I take off my shoes and stretch out aching insteps. I make mint tea and sit on the sofa, watching clouds lit by a half moon float across the sky. There's still a light coming from the top floor of the house across the gardens and where a man and a woman sit at a table, talking.

I love my home, and enjoy living here alone but tonight I wish I wasn't getting into bed by myself again. When I go out to parties, especially ones where I know there'll be new faces, there's always this seed of hope in the back of my mind that maybe tonight I'll meet someone.

Tomorrow's Sunday and I don't have plans during the day. I'll probably go to the gym then do my weekly shop. I picture my ideal day: lying in bed with my boyfriend all morning, then brunch in Primrose Hill, followed by a long walk on the Heath or through Regent's Park, enjoying this early spring weather.

From my bedroom I hear the distant rumble of a late-night train. The occasional car passes by, its headlights leaking a brief glow of light through the small gap between the edge of the slatted metal blinds and the window. Otherwise, it's silent.

I'm about to take my top off when I notice that a couple of the gold sequins around the neckline have come loose. I touch them, and my index and middle fingers come to rest on the bare skin just above the fabric.

Shocked, they spring away.

Then, anxiously, they return. Slowly they trace the surrounding skin, seeking reassurance that there are other places like this, that it's just the nature of this unfamiliar terrain. Everywhere else the skin is smooth and soft. Here, in an area a few centimetres above my left nipple it looks the same. But under my fingers it's hard as ice.

2

I turn out the light, quickly take off my clothes and get into bed. I'm shivering. I wrap the duvet tightly around me, trying to swaddle myself with its warmth. But I can't stop shaking. Closing my eyes, I will myself to forget what my fingers have read. It's all I can see. I picture it growing bigger, staining my whole body.

I think about all the things I could lose. What if I never have the chance to fall in love again?

I curl myself into a ball and try to sleep, but my mind's racing. Usually when I can't sleep I put on the light and read but tonight I want to distance myself from my body and this room. This room, with its high corniced ceilings, white walls, wood floor and old fireplace has always been my sanctuary. Suddenly it's oppressive, frightening.

When daylight starts to spill around the edge of the window, I'm still awake. I've only been in bed around four hours but it's been the longest night. I listen to the murmurings of the outside world as it slowly comes to life again. The birds are singing, newspapers thud onto doorsteps, and a crying child is comforted by his father.

I spend most of the day in bed. Running on the treadmill at the gym, trying to make my body leaner and healthier, knowing there's this thing lurking under my skin seems wrong. I'm supposed to be meeting my sister, Tanya, and a friend this evening for a movie and dinner. I think about cancelling, but in the end decide it might be better to be around people than alone with my mind. And I haven't seen my sister for a couple of weeks which, for us, is a long time.

I leave the flat at six. It's still light and on my way to Camden Town I walk past the Victorian redbrick terraces of South Hampstead, the roundabout at Swiss Cottage and through Primrose Hill. This is my patch of London. As children, my sister, two years younger, and I had piano lessons on the first floor of one of the redbrick houses I pass. As a teenager I spent long days revising in the curved concrete-finned library building that edges the roundabout, and weekends wandering up and down Camden High street looking for red-tab Levis, Bob Dylan albums and silver hoop earrings. My earliest memories are of afternoons in Primrose Hill with my mother, lying on the grey rug I think she still has. This evening the outside world looks the same as it always has. Except it no longer feels quite so solid.

Everyone else in the cinema laughs their way through *The Royal Tenenbaums* where a father who walked out on his family years earlier tries to be reunited with them by pretending he's dying of stomach cancer. I shudder every time the word cancer's mentioned, a sick sensation rising in the back of my throat.

Tanya's booked dinner at a Caribbean restaurant called The Mango Room. She came with her husband, Axel, a few weeks ago.

'You've got to try the strawberry daiquiri. Axel loved it.'

It is all delicious but I can only pick at my snapper in mango and coconut sauce. I look around the crowded restaurant, all the tables jammed with people eating and drinking and laughing and wish I'd stayed home.

'Don't you like it?' asks Tanya, surprised by my unusual lack of appetite.

I pretend I had a big lunch. I think about telling her but know how worried she'd get. I want my mother. She'd know what to do. But she and my dad are on holiday.

The next morning, I surprise myself by calling the doctors' surgery before work. I'd always thought I'd be the type of person who'd go into denial if something like this happened. Ignore it in the hope it might go away. They tell me my usual GP's away for three weeks and offer an appointment with someone I don't know. I refuse it, deciding I'd rather wait until I see my mother again and see what she suggests. She considers herself a fountain of medical knowledge even though, as my father continually reminds her, most of it's based on hearsay and what she's read in the papers.

My phone's already ringing when I arrive at work. It's George, the client for the new beauty spa we're designing at Harrods. I'm the project architect.

'Good, doll, I'm glad you're in. I had a brainwave over the weekend. You know that space behind the lounge area. Instead of getting in yet another brand I think we should turn it into a Medical Spa. Somewhere you can pop in and get a bit of Botox in your lunch hour. There's already huge demand. It's only going to get bigger. Fax me the plans now so I can check the sizes work.'

I spend the rest of the day working on a set of drawings of the black steel counters for the hair salon. George calls at least once an hour. 'Have you finished them yet? I need them like yesterday, sweetheart.' Today, I'm grateful not to have time to think about anything else and to have to stay at the office until nine.

Later, alone in my flat, I tentatively reach my hand under my clothes. I haven't been there since Saturday night. Slowly, I move my fingers towards my skin thinking, please make it be gone. But it isn't. And that sick sensation rises in the back of my throat again. I run my fingers over and over it, like a worry bead, while wishing my touch could dissolve it.

During the day I leave my body behind. Work is frantic. George calls constantly, now from his boat in the South of France, to talk about his various brainwaves. In the brief pauses when I'm not thinking about the design of a Chakra Balancing Room or a manicure table, I try and persuade myself that it's just a hormonal fluctuation. I once read in a magazine that nine out of ten breast lumps are non-malignant and I repeat this to myself like a mantra. At times I think I'm going mad and just creating a huge melodrama in my head.

But in the evenings, when I return to my body and my fingers tell me nothing has changed, I get scared again.

Two things happened recently, which at the time I didn't pay much attention to. Now they keep coming back to me. I was out on a date a few weeks ago. In a crowded Soho bar, he said to me, 'There's something very other-worldly and ethereal about you.' I didn't fancy him but was flattered. It made me sound both mysterious and calm, an intriguing combination, though I'm not sure I'm either. Now his words make me think of someone who's about to disappear and, in a slightly crazed state, I start convincing myself that this clean-cut Greek economics professor was some sort of psychic.

It was Easter last weekend, and on Good Friday I went to a performance of Bach's *St Matthew* Passion with my family. It was at St George's on Hanover Square, the church my sister and Axel were married in last summer. Towards the end, as the choir lamented Jesus's death, I had the strangest vision of my own funeral taking place in this church. I saw my coffin being carried down the aisle. Now I'm convinced I'm psychic too. Or just mad.

I tell no one for over a week, curling my secret tightly inside me.

9

The following Saturday, I fly to Zurich with Tanya and Axel. We're meeting my parents there and going to a big family party, being held by mum's cousins.

Lots of her relatives live there. Her side of the family are Jewish, German-born, but had to escape the Nazis in the thirties. Most of them came to Zurich, but Mum and her mother went to Rio de Janeiro as her uncle lived there. She arrived in London twenty years later, on a cold January day in the late fifties, married a Yorkshireman a decade later, and has never left.

The party's not until Sunday lunchtime and on Saturday evening my parents take us to a restaurant overlooking Lake Zurich. Over dinner, my sister starts talking about the film we saw last weekend and how funny it was.

'Why do you have to go on and on about it?' I say, not wanting to be reminded.

'I can talk about whatever I want.' She's surprised and hurt by my sudden outburst. I apologise but later my mother says, 'I don't understand you. We're here for a nice weekend and you've been irritable from the moment we arrived.'

I thought I'd hidden it well. But somehow, she always seems to be able to pick up on things. I want to tell her but we're never alone. And as long as she doesn't know, it can still be just a story in my mind.

The party's in a beautiful sixties house in the hills above the lake. Before lunch there's champagne and one of my younger cousins, a music student, plays a Mozart violin sonata. It's a sunny day and the large sliding glass doors onto the garden are open.

At the dessert buffet, I pile my plate with white chocolate mousse and profiteroles, while thinking didn't some woman write a book recently about how dairy products can cause breast cancer? Well, if I've got it already, I'm probably going to die, so I may as well eat what I want.

My parents and I leave for London on Sunday evening. Tanya and Axel are staying on an extra night to see a friend. The flight's delayed and my mother manages to talk her way into the Swissair executive lounge as my father stands back, embarrassed by what he affectionately calls her 'foreign pushiness.'

'Come on, let's have a glass of wine.' Mum starts chatting to me about the party and all the people we've seen. My father's a couple of seats away, engrossed in yesterday's *Financial Times*.

I interrupt her.

'There's something I need to talk to you about.'

'What's wrong?'

'I found a lump in my breast.' I look across the green upholstered seats. It is strange to be voicing this, for the first time, in an airport lounge.

'When?'

'A week ago.'

'You should have told me. You must go to the doctor.' Then in a more relaxed tone, which surprises me, she adds, 'I'm sure it's nothing, though. Most lumps turn out to be benign, especially at your age. And it's not as if we have any family history of breast cancer.'

The next morning, she calls the private GP she occasionally uses and gets me an appointment for Thursday. Her words soothed me. I'm still scared but no longer consumed by visions of my impending death.

I've never met this doctor but she's explained why I'm coming. We're so busy at work that I even feel a bit guilty for taking the time off.

11

It's very different to the NHS. He tries to put me at ease by making small talk, asking where I live and what I do, initially making no mention of the real reason I'm here.

'How lovely,' he says when he hears I'm an architect. 'So, what's your favourite modern building in London?'

Get a move on. I'm here to find out whether I have cancer, not to have a chat about modern architecture.

But I tell him how much I like the Royal College of Physicians, a building designed in the sixties by an architect called Denys Lasdun. I designed a memorial chapel in its gardens for one of my university projects.

A few minutes later, almost as an aside, he says, 'Let me have a quick look at you.' I take off my top, lie down on the bed and direct my eyes towards the ceiling. It's the first time I've exposed my breasts to a doctor and I'm embarrassed, even though I know he sees this all the time.

His fingers, warm and slightly moist, move methodically across my breasts and under my arms, squeezing and probing. He is silent. Then they return to the area above my left nipple and stay there for what seems like ages. All he says is, 'Try and breathe normally.' It's only then I realise I've been holding my breath.

I'm dreading his response. Is he going to tell me it's huge and send me straight to hospital?

Eventually, he removes his hands from my skin. 'There's definitely a lump. The good news is it feels small and not at all suspicious. It's smooth and mobile, which cancer usually isn't. I'd guess it's just a cyst. We'll arrange for you to see a surgeon, though. Just as a precaution.'

It's one of the best pieces of news I've ever had.

When I get to work there are a couple of messages from George. I call him back. He's in high spirits.

'I've just convinced Swarovski to do the crystals for the Hospitality Room. I'm going to have strings of them lining all the walls. It'll be fab.'

Excitedly, he tells me about his plans for the room.

'I'll hire it out for special day packages. Like hen parties - treatments and champagne all day long. Then we'll take them home in a limo.'

It seems like a good moment to ask a favour.

'George, I read in *Vogue* how Harrods are now doing that Yuko Hair Straightening System. I really want to try it. Any chance of a special price?' George is always trying to negotiate a good deal himself.

'If you get the fish-tank drawings for Creme de la Mer out by the end of the week, I'll introduce you to Jacques, our Yuko man, after the site meeting on Monday. We'll see what we can do.'

Jacques runs his hands through my shoulder length hair.

'This no good. We cannot do the Yuko. Your hair is so dry and curly already. All this colour has really damaged it. The only way you will ever be able to do the Yuko is to completely grow out this hair and replace it with the new.'

In the past couple of years, my hair's gone from its natural dark brown to auburn and then blonde. More recently, I got tired of seeing an almost continuous stripe of roots so I've gone a bit darker again.

As a consolation, George offers me a free haircut instead. 'I'll get Vladimir to do it. He's our best cutter.'

I'm tempted to say no. I have an appointment with the specialist tomorrow and if by any chance I were to get diagnosed with cancer, I want to cling on to every millimetre of hair for as long as possible. Baldness. That is what I associate with it. And I can't help having the superstitious view that if I do have it cut I will end up with cancer and if I don't I won't. But in the end, it's too good an offer to refuse.

I've never spent much time on Harley Street but I know the streets parallel to it well. I often go to the Royal Institute of British Architects on Portland Place for books and lectures, to Marylebone High Street for shampoo and organic soup at Aveda or almond croissants and cappuccinos at Patisserie Valerie.

Of Harley Street, I know only the outer skin, a series of brick and stone terraced houses with engraved brass plaques next to their front doors. It's a street I sometimes go down on my way to the West End.

Today, as I walk down the street, I notice the black railings in front of each building. Their spiky points seem threatening. I look through the gaps between them down into basements. Most of these windows are grilled, curtained or frosted, but a couple of times I catch a glimpse of a room filled with large pieces of equipment. Above ground, many of the interiors are also shrouded by sheer curtains or blinds. What happens in these spaces? Behind these discrete and dignified facades do people sometimes get told they only have months left?

Not at all suspicious. The GP's words come reassuringly back into my head.

A memory surfaces. It's the late May Bank Holiday Monday, almost three years ago. A humid afternoon wrapped by a closed sullen sky. I'm at The London Clinic, a private hospital near Harley Street, with my parents. We're visiting one of their best friends. He has cancer.

Inside his room it's cool and dark and the sharp edges of his body are visible beneath a white crocheted blanket. He doesn't say much. We tell him how well he looks even though we know he's probably dying. We stay an hour and then I take my parents to The Conran Shop round the corner where they help me

14

choose a light for my new flat. We walk down Marylebone High Street, past shops and cafes busy with holiday crowds. I take in all the activity around me and think of our friend in his quiet hospital room. With some sadness, I realise how porous the membrane between these two worlds actually is.

The surgeon's waiting room is empty. It has deep floral-patterned sofas with matching curtains. There are framed cartoons on the walls and neat stacks of *Country Life* magazines on the table.

A nurse in a blue uniform leads me down the corridor and into a large room at the back of the building. I take a seat on one side of a broad mahogany desk. On it are several silver photo frames filled with pictures of smiling children. The consultant comes in, his tall frame encased in a lightweight beige suit. There's a maroon silk handkerchief in the breast pocket and a matching cravat round his neck. He holds out a big hand with long tapered fingers and clasps it round mine.

'So, you're an architect. Where do you work?'

'For a small practice in Clerkenwell.'

'Great part of town. I used to be at Barts, behind the meat market. It's changed a lot since my day, though. And where did you study?'

'Cambridge.'

'That must have been fun. Now go behind the curtains and get changed so I can have a look.'

There's a bed hidden behind them. I'm lying on it bare-chested and a little shivery when his bulk appears between the frilly pink and white curtains. He rubs his hands together and begins to make circular movements across my skin.

Almost immediately he says, 'I'm impressed you even managed to find this. I doubt there's anything to worry about.

We'll do a fine needle aspiration and an ultrasound, just to be absolutely sure.'

I wince as he plunges a syringe into my left breast. I watch it fill with blood and he explains it's so they can examine some of the cells in the lump.

In a basement room, a different doctor smears gel over my left breast and glides a probe across it. He tells me he can see a lump but that it looks completely normal. I relax and look at the screen. A series of black and white images shift across it. They look like the ripples and dunes of a desert landscape seen from above, shadow and sunlight cast across their surface. The hidden geography of my body.

I return for my results. The surgeon reads from the report:

'"No sonographic features, especially of malignancy, are seen…" It's definitely not cancer. *Thank God.* I expect it's a fibroadenoma, a benign lump. The pathology from the needle aspiration did pick up some slightly unusual cells, but they didn't even categorise them as suspicious yet alone cancerous. So, nothing to worry about. Best if I take it out anyway, though. Just a night in hospital and back to work a day or two later.'

I arrange to have the operation in a couple of weeks, as soon as I'm back from New York. I'm visiting my friend Paul there over the May Bank Holiday weekend.

It's a beautiful spring morning. I should go straight to work but I want to hold on to the sweetness of this moment. I walk to Villandry on Great Portland Street and order a cappuccino. Morning light streams in through the large windows, softening the dark wood interior. I feel every particle of sunlight on my face, taste every drop of coffee on my tongue, as my hands slowly leaf through the morning paper.

3

I met Paul through Ioana a couple of years ago while he was working in London as an environmental designer. He's very tall and nice-looking, in a blue-eyed, blonde-haired wholesome American kind of way. He's also bright and interesting with an easy-going manner. He called soon after we first met to see if I wanted to have lunch. Might he be a possible boyfriend? But it seemed like the chemistry wasn't quite there on either side. Instead, we became good friends.

He was always arranging things. Laksa parties at his house off Ladbroke Grove in the winter and barbeques there in summer. Drinks in Hoxton Square on a Friday evening followed by Vietnamese food on Kingsland Road. Saturday mornings at Café Lisboa on Golborne Road for coffee and bright yellow *pastis de natas.*

It was a lot of fun having him around and I was disappointed when he left one summer, to set up the New York office for his company.

I've got a great apartment in Queens, he emailed. *Come and stay whenever you want. It's cool being back but I'm really missing my London friends.*

I land in Newark at midnight on Friday. There are no more buses into Manhattan so I share a limo with a group of girls who've come for a hen weekend. I text Paul, who's still out with his friends, and tell him to meet me outside the Marriot Hotel on Times Square.

As I wait for Paul, I take in the night city. The surfaces of the buildings around me are a veil of coloured neon. Glittering billboards advertise Coke, Kodak, TGI Fridays. Cab horns honk away and I watch traffic and people swirl around me. I think back over the past few weeks in London and remind myself how lucky I am to have been able to walk away free, to be back in the world in which I belong.

Bright sunlight and jetlag wake me early the next morning. I'm staying in Paul's living room and the windows are bare. Facing east, they frame the Manhattan skyline. When I sit up in bed, the Empire State building's directly in front of me. It's almost a picture postcard view of Manhattan. But to my left is an empty slot of sky where, until eight months ago, the Twin Towers stood.

I'm exhausted but too excited to go back to sleep.

'So, what do you fancy doing?' asks Paul when he's up.

'I'd love to see the Gerhard Richter show at MoMA. Apart from that, nothing in particular. Have you got stuff planned?'

'I've told a couple of friends we'll meet them for breakfast at this great diner round the corner. Tonight there's an opening at a gallery in Chelsea we could go to. And a crowd's doing brunch at Veselka in the East Village tomorrow - known for the best pancakes in town. Otherwise, I'm all yours.'

After breakfast, Paul and I take the overground into Manhattan and walk through Central Park towards MoMA. It's almost too hot and the park's crowded with jugglers, buskers, lovers, children and softball players.

At the heart of the Gerhard Richter show is a striking series of black and white paintings about a group of terrorists who died in a Stuttgart prison in the seventies. They have titles like *Dead*, *Hanged*, and *Funeral*. So many of the paintings in the exhibition

18

seem to be about absence, both in their subject matter, and the ghostly way in which they've been painted. I can't help but think of 9/11. It's so easy to forget it happened when you're here. Apart from the gap in the skyline, New York still seems just the same.

We keep walking through the city. Later in the afternoon we buy burritos and eat them on the grass in Union Square. The Hari Krishnas parade past, dancing and singing in their orange robes. Next to us, two men are chatting. 'I just don't know what to do,' the balding one says to his friend, 'I've got this enormous crush on my shrink.' Paul and I catch one another's eye and smile. 'How very New York,' I say quietly.

For the next few days, I saturate myself in the sunshine and noise of this city. I remember my first visit here, in nineteen eighty-four, with my parents and sister. I was so excited by the canyon-like streets, the neon, and the way the shops stayed open past dark. This time, I wander round different neighbourhoods, visit the Guggenheim, go to a Jivamukti yoga class in Soho, get a manicure from a Korean nail bar, buy discounted Seven jeans and Miu Miu sandals, hang out in a vegan restaurant on the Upper East side.

I take in a kaleidoscope of images:

Walking down a black tarmac pier on the Hudson River at sunset and sensing the city fall away. The high-level train track looping crazily between the old Chelsea warehouse buildings. The butterfly wings preserved in blocks of resin at the gallery opening on Saturday evening. The interior of the Campbell Apartment, a tiny twenties cocktail bar at the top of Grand Central Station, where the amber of our Long Island Iced Teas mirrors the colour of its wood panelled walls. And in Greenwich Village, a wire fence draped with hand-written notes, flowers and photographs. A reminder of how behind its still gleaming facades this city holds so many other stories.

I mean to visit Ground Zero on my last day to see the scar that had been left behind. On aerial photos, embedded within the urban fabric, I am always surprised by how small it actually seems. In the end, I run out of time as I am too busy shopping.

I get home the day before the operation. While I was in New York I'd almost forgotten I was having it. There's a card from one of my best friends waiting.

Dearest Annabel, I hope everything goes well on Thursday. Just remember I'll always be here for you. All my love, Paola xx.

I'm very touched, as well as surprised by her concern. It's just a routine procedure.

I call my friend Catherine to discuss our weekend plans to go to Bath to stay at her in-laws' cottage.

'I'll be out of hospital Friday morning. I'm definitely still on for coming down on Saturday. A chilled-out weekend should be the perfect way to recover.'

My mother offers to take me to hospital.

I tell her I'm going to the yoga class I normally do on Thursdays before work, and ask if she can pick me up from there.

'You shouldn't be doing yoga just before an operation, especially all jet lagged. You should be at home relaxing.'

'Yoga is relaxing. Anyway, I'll have all day to do that in hospital.'

On the way there, I tell her what a great time I had in New York.

'So, did anything happen between you and Paul?' She pretends to sound uninterested.

I sigh. 'I've told you before, we're just good friends. These days that is actually possible.'

'Well I thought maybe as you were staying in his flat...' What, that we'd end up having rampant sex?

My mother has never understood how you can meet an attractive, intelligent, nice man and not at least give them a chance. It's an ongoing discussion.

'The chemistry's just not there.'

'But you can grow to like someone.'

'Anyway,' she continues. 'I meant to tell you I'm not that happy about you rushing off to Bath. You should come home and stay with us.'

'Don't fuss so much. Catherine's seven months pregnant. It's not exactly going to be a wild weekend.'

I've spent very little time in hospitals, and never been admitted to one myself. This one's private and feels more like a hotel. It's being paid for by the medical insurance my mother persuaded me to take out. A few others are waiting to be checked in. There's a woman of around forty with hairdresser straight hair and manicured nails, which she's anxiously tapping on the arm of her chair. I overhear her tell the receptionist she's also with my surgeon. Poor thing, I think, maybe she has breast cancer.

I'm intrigued to at last be a patient. I move the bed up and down, check out the cable TV and smile as a nurse asks whether I have any prostheses or hearing aids. People come in and out of my room. There's a woman with menus, an Irish nurse who says she's in charge of all the surgeon's patients, the anaesthetist, and, finally, the surgeon. He takes out his felt tip pen and marks my left breast with a large black cross.

'Don't worry, it definitely isn't cancer,' he says as he leaves the room.

Paola, who lives round the corner and often works from home, stops by to say hello.

'I'll come back tomorrow morning. Perhaps we can have a coffee at Aveda after you're out.'

I'm quite looking forward to a day off work.

21

My mother offers to stay so she can be with me when I come round, but I tell her to go home as it could be hours before they operate. I promise to call as soon as I'm fully awake.

It's early afternoon when they roll a metal trolley into my room and take me down to the basement. I'm crammed into a small room whose walls are lined high with boxes of medical supplies. As I wait, I'm not scared, just bored. It's ages until the anaesthetist comes in and says, 'I'm just going to give your hand a small scratch and next thing you know it'll all be over.'

My feet are shaking. I open my eyes. I'm in a long room, lying on one of a row of trolleys. I hear the surgeon's voice in the background,

'Take her back to her room as soon as possible.'

A nurse starts rolling me out and I realise they were talking about me.

I'm drowsy and relaxed. There's no pain. I lie in bed and enjoy the peace, this feeling of not needing to do anything at all. I should call my mother and tell her I'm fine, but I want to stay in this quiet space a little longer.

The door to my room opens and the surgeon marches in, accompanied by the Irish nurse. He's still wearing his green scrubs. I wait for him to tell me how well it's gone. He goes into the bathroom, washes his hands, comes back in and stands at the foot of my bed.

'Well it's lucky we took it out. Nasty little bugger. I told my pathologist it didn't look quite right as soon as I cut into it. The preliminary frozen sections from the operation unfortunately showed some pre-cancerous cells.' He pauses.

'It's possible there's cancer there, too. We won't know until Monday when the full biopsy's back.'

His words are a gunshot, quivering across my skin and plunging into my stomach.

'But you promised it wasn't.'

'I'm as surprised as you.'

The difference is it doesn't really matter for you, does it?

He looks at my feet with their scuffed crimson painted nails exposed beyond the end of the sheet and says, 'Your poor little toes,' covers them up, and leaves the room.

4

The nurse stays behind. She looks sadly at me, the large dark irises of her eyes floating in the curtained half-light.

'Would you like a cup of tea?'

'Yes please.' I don't know what else to say.

She goes out to get the tea I don't want. While she's gone, I keep replaying the moment the surgeon came into my room, obliterating what happened with what should have happened. I hear his voice reassuringly say, *Just as I suspected, a benign lump.* And all I wish is that I could erase what did actually happen in that tiny slice of time.

I want my mother. But she won't come until I call her, and if I call her, I'll have to tell her. And hurt her.

I get the answer machine with the British Telecom lady's infuriatingly polite voice. Several tries later she picks up, sounding rushed.

'Sorry, darling, did you try before? I just popped out. How did it go?'

She arrives within minutes.

'Are you sure they haven't made a mistake and got you mixed up with someone else?' is the first thing she asks.

'I told you, he said he saw it himself.' My voice is flat.

'I'm going to try and find out what's really going on.'

I hear their voices in the corridor. Then she comes back in.

'He says so far he's only seen some precancerous cells and it's possible there may not even be any actual cancer.' She sits down by my bed. 'Perhaps it's not the end of the world.'

Soon, my friend Anat arrives, carrying a bunch of red and yellow tulips. *Hooray, have escaped!* she texted half an hour earlier. *Today you take priority over my roofing details! Xx*

'Hello, darling Bella.' Then she looks at my face. 'What's happened?'

'They think I might have cancer.'

The tulips fall from her hand. They lie briefly on the floor, their petals crushed against it.

My mother is telling her that we don't know much yet, and it may just be some pre-cancerous cells. Then Ioana turns up in a sober navy work suit. I haven't seen her since that night out on Charlotte Street when we were both wearing heels and low-cut tops. She's brought me chocolate brownies and the latest *Vogue*. I watch her face also change.

They both try to reassure my mother, telling her how they know people who've had pre-cancerous cells on their cervix and are absolutely fine. I don't say much. The anaesthetic and the shock have made everything seem disconnected and remote.

My mother's good at putting on a brave face and hiding her fear. When my father and sister arrive, they are more transparent. Which makes it more painful. He kisses my head and says, 'My poor Annabel,' and then retreats to a corner chair where he sits, his head slightly hung, briefcase by his side, not really joining in the conversation. Both his parents died of cancer. My sister's sitting on the floor, as all the chairs are taken. Her blue eyes are stained with tears. Axel crouches next to her stroking her blonde hair.

She's the last to leave.

'Shall I stay the night? I could sleep in your bed with you.'

Her sadness will only make me sadder.

25

'That's so sweet but I'm shattered. Let's both just try and get some sleep.'

She hugs me. 'Oh, Mooki.' It's her pet name for me. 'I love you so much.'

Of course I don't sleep. In the silence of the night, I can feel myself falling, falling towards a world to which I thought I didn't belong.

I've seen others get trapped in that world.

There was Kitty, a friend of my mother's, who got pancreatic cancer when I was about eight. One Saturday afternoon, after my parents had dragged me and my sister round the antique shops on Camden Passage in Islington, Mum decided we'd stop by the hospital as we were nearby. When we arrived, they told us she died, quite suddenly, that morning. The image of her empty bed, perhaps still holding the imprint, smell and warmth of her lost body stayed with me.

My dad's father died of bone cancer when I was two. His mother was diagnosed with throat cancer when I was sixteen. They inserted a tracheotomy in her throat, which reduced her voice to a whisper and her meals to liquids.

Towards the end, she was treated in the head and neck ward at The Royal Marsden. When the doctors said they couldn't do any more, she went home to Yorkshire. One dull January afternoon, my parents rushed up there. The next morning, I was listening to Chrissie Hynde, my teenage heroine, singing 'Hymn to Her' on my Walkman, when I was told my grandmother had died.

More recently, there was my parents' friend, whom I visited in hospital that May afternoon three years earlier. On a beautiful early September morning, my mother called to tell me that he spent his last night coughing up blood and had died at dawn. Just a few miles across town, I'd also been up all night, drawing up an architecture competition entry I'd done with a friend, for the redevelopment of a disused viaduct near Brick Lane. As I walked to the Tube on my way to work, exhausted yet alert, everything around me seemed heightened. I saw the beauty in things I normally didn't notice, like the bright pinks and reds of the geraniums on a windowsill, the shadows of trees lying across the pavement.

The problem is, no one I know who's had cancer has escaped.

I also remember what my mother once said to me after I told her about the friend of a friend who died of lung cancer at twenty-five.

'The younger you are the more aggressive it often is. It's very unfair.'

The ping-pong noise of patients ringing their bells cuts repeatedly through the otherwise silent hospital. We're all hidden behind closed doors. Are there others going through something similar?

The nurses check on me every couple of hours. Most of them are my age or younger. They're polite but distant, just asking if my wound hurts and whether I need painkillers. The physical pain's minimal so each time I say no.

I fall asleep around four. A nurse I haven't seen before wakes me up at six-thirty.

'We need you up and ready. You've got a busy morning. The taxi's coming at half seven to take you round the corner to Harley Street for the bone scan. You'll come back here for the chest X-Ray. Then it's Harley Street again for a liver ultrasound. After that, you can go home.'

'Why am I having all these tests?'

'They need to check the cancer hasn't spread. It's standard procedure for someone in your situation.'

Her words slam into me with a sickening thud. *Cancer. Spread. Your situation.*

A few minutes later, the anaesthetist comes in. At first, I don't recognise him. He smells of expensive aftershave and has a suit and tie on, in place of the gown and school dinner lady cap from yesterday.

'Why am I not being told everything?' I'm angry. 'Yesterday it was possibly just pre-cancer. Today it might be secondary cancer.'

'We still don't know whether it's cancer or not. We *always* do these tests if we find anything at all. It's a precaution. I'll be extremely surprised if yours don't all come back completely clear.'

'How can I believe that? Less than twenty-four hours ago I was told I definitely didn't have cancer'

'Listen, I know it's hard but you're going to have to try and be positive about this. It's the most important thing. I'm going to tell you a story, about a world-famous pianist. She had breast cancer a few years ago. I won't tell you her name, but what I will say is that she's now playing better than ever.'

To me, his words sound ridiculous. How can life be better after cancer? You either get sicker and sicker and then die. Or you might get tricked into thinking you're better for a bit, like my grandmother did, but sooner or later it catches up with you again.

On Harley Street, I'm injected with radioactive dye and then taken into a white room and told to lie face up on a metal bed protruding out of a large white cylinder.

'You must remain completely still while you're in the tunnel,' the radiographer tells me.

It starts to move, slowly swallowing my body, centimetre by centimetre. It's dark and tight inside and I don't know where it ends. It clicks and groans as it maps my skeleton. I'm starting to learn there's a deep loneliness to this illness and its procedures.

When it's over, the woman says, 'You can go now. Have a nice weekend.' I ask if she can give me the results.

'Sorry, I can't do that. Your doctor will tell you next week.' And I'm terrified she's seen something horrible.

Back at the hospital, a nurse takes me down to the basement for the lung X-Ray.

'Don't worry too much about it. I saw on your form you're a non-smoker. I'm sure you'll be fine.'

Guiltily, I remember myself as a teenager, bunking off sports lessons to go and smoke, eat chips and drink bitter lukewarm tea at a horrible greasy spoon near school. It was where all the cool girls went, and I, someone on the fringes of that crowd, was always pleased to be included. I'd smoked on and off until my mid-twenties, mostly at parties or on the nights I stayed up late to work.

Breakfast TV drones on in the waiting area. A home improvement programme is showing how to give an old table a new lease of life by gluing leaves onto it and varnishing it. Who cares.

I slump into a corner seat. The old man next to me asks what's wrong.

'Listen, my dear. I had colon cancer three years ago. When they first told me I thought OK, old boy, it's curtains for you now. I've been clear ever since. I'm sure everything will work out fine for you, too.'

I'm touched by how this stranger's shared his story. But he's at least seventy and I'm thirty-one. Greedily, I'm thinking I need a lot more than three years. Another fifty might just about do.

It's ages until they call me through, hand me a blue gown, and tell me to strip to the waist.

I stand in front of the X-Ray machine, being barked instructions on how to position my body.

'Arms up like this and stand completely still.'

'Turn around ninety degrees.

'No, I said ninety not a hundred and eighty'

The woman doing the X-Rays is really grumpy. Maybe she had a bad Tube journey? Got PMT? How fucking awful for her.

When I come out, I notice a slim young woman with glossy black hair, wearing a fitted black jacket and jeans, sitting in the waiting area reading the paper. When she looks up, I realise it's Paola. I almost run towards her.

'They told me I'd find you down here. What's going on? You look as if you've lost about four stone overnight.'

She puts her arms around me as I mutter, 'Testing for secondaries...won't give me the results...they don't give a shit.'

She takes me back upstairs. The door to the room opposite mine is half open. I recognise the woman I saw in reception yesterday morning. She's sitting on her bed wearing a pink satin nightdress and a matching dressing gown. Her husband, in a suit and tie, clasps her hand and looks at her face as she looks down. They are both silent.

I have the liver ultrasound at the surgeon's offices on Harley Street, lying on the same bed where a couple of weeks ago they scanned my left breast. Today, I can't stop shaking. The nurse places a white crocheted blanket over me as the doctor positions the gelled probe at the top of my right ribcage and glides it across my skin. Today, I turn my head as I can't bear to look at the images on the screen.

I'm discharged for the weekend. My mother collects me. It's a perfect May day. We drive home along the edge of Regent's Park. Behind filigree hedges and gaps between railings I catch glimpses of people sitting on the grass or boating on the lake. This pleasure garden now seems like an image to which I no longer belong.

Later that day, I hear news on the radio of a train crash at Potters Bar. Seven dead. Hearing this softens my own pain. At least I'm still here.

I'll have to wait until Monday morning for my results. Unable to bear worrying for the next two days that I've got advanced cancer, I'm trying to convince myself that it'll just be pre-cancer. *Just* pre-cancer. Before yesterday that would have completely freaked me out. But now, compared to the other possibilities, it'd be a relief. From what I've discovered on Google, it's not life threatening and non-invasive, although the not so good news is that it can sometimes become the real thing.

Not wanting to spend any time alone, I've gratefully accepted invitations from the few friends who know what's happened. I go to Ayala's barbeque on Saturday lunchtime and in the evening, Paola takes me out to dinner at The Organic Café in Queen's Park where we eat mushroom risotto and drink white wine. On Sunday, I have lunch with Anat at my favourite pub, The Lansdowne in Primrose Hill. She even makes me laugh with a story about a recent blind date where the guy sat through dinner taking constant calls on his mobile and then had the nerve to ask her back to his place. 'And he was a nice Jewish boy from Hampstead. What a *Schmuck*.'

That evening, I go to a dinner party at Ioana's in Notting Hill, where I don't mention what's happened to anyone else. In any other situation, it would have been a lovely relaxing weekend.

On Monday morning I'm still telling myself it's just pre-cancer. Anything else is way too scary. My mother wants to come to the appointment but I've told her I'd rather go alone.

'How are you today?' the surgeon asks.

'That depends on what you say.'

31

He pauses. A small space opens up, which still offers the possibility of hearing it's all been a mistake, or that just a couple of pre-cancerous cells have been found in an otherwise normal lump.

'I'm so sorry to have to tell you this,' he says, gently, 'but we have found cancer.'

There's a finality to those words. As if a door has suddenly slammed shut.

He reads off a sheet of paper.

'"4 millimetres of *ductal carcinoma* insitu grade 3. 11 millimetres of invasive *ductal carcinoma* grades 2 and 3." Your bones, liver and lungs are clear, though.'

He places the report back down on the table. It has the logo of a butterfly in the top right corner and the letterhead belongs to a man called Clive in Harpenden. My name is clearly printed below.

'What does that mean?'

'Your tumour's a mix of pre-cancer and cancerous cells. Insitu's the pre and invasive's the cancer. It's always graded from one to three. One's the least aggressive, three's the most.'

He's talking at me. '...propose to perform a segmental mastectomy of your left breast...need to see if it's spread to the lymph nodes or any of the tissue beyond the edges of the tumour...'

I hear only one word.

Mastectomy.

Butchered, desecrated, lopsided, undesirable.

No more boyfriends, low cut tops, beach holidays, communal changing rooms.

'A mastectomy?'

'I only intend to remove part of your breast. It'll be like taking a slice out of an orange.'

I'm so relieved he's not planning to chop my breast off that I forget to ask whether it means I'll be left with a dent where the missing slice of orange used to be.

'So, when do you want it? I operate on Tuesdays and Thursdays.'

'Tomorrow.'

'My list's fairly full, but as it's you I'll do it. It'll be two nights in this time. Now, you need to go downstairs and get a mammogram and an ultrasound on the right side so we can check nothing's going on there.'

As I'm leaving, he puts his hand on my shoulder and says, 'It'll be OK, we'll sort you out.' Right now, it doesn't feel OK at all.

I press my ribs against the cool black steel of the machine. The radiographer's hands pick up my breast and spread it onto the metal plate as if it were clay. A sheet of clear Perspex moves down and sandwiches it painfully into place.

'Right hand on your tummy and stay still. All right pet.'

Click.

She rotates the machine so the plate's on the diagonal and pours my breast back in.

'Left hand on your head and stay still. All right pet.'

Click.

If she says all right pet in that stupid chirpy voice one more time, I'm going to fucking kill her.

'You can get dressed now. All right pet.'

In another room, the doctor scans my right breast. Ominously, he returns the probe to one particular area. I hear the click of the mouse as he blows up an image on the screen.

'There seems to be a small lump here.' His tone is neutral.

Will it just keep getting worse? Am I like one of those apples which are bright and shiny on the outside, but all rotten when you cut them open?

'It looks completely normal. I'll do a needle biopsy just to make sure.'

I've heard those words before. Last time, I believed them.

A nurse is waiting outside the room. She takes me to a large room on the first floor. It's furnished like an expensive drawing room, with plush carpets and deep sofas but there's an emptiness to it. It echoes with sadness as if its walls had secreted too many stories of disappointment and broken dreams.

We sit down on the sofa and she asks if I have any questions. There's a box of tissues on the coffee table. But I can't even cry. All I can tell myself is that they must have made a terrible mistake and got my results mixed up with someone else's and after tomorrow's operation they'll finally realise.

My mother's parked outside, a few metres beyond the surgeon's rooms. I walk down the steps and pause on the pavement for a moment. I want to stay where I am, retain this space between us. The concrete paving stones, parking meters and cars form a gap, which maintain her ignorance and my dream that it isn't really true.

I walk slowly towards her, and in a few seconds the gap has collapsed.

5

I don't cry. My mother responds by being practical. 'You need to call the insurance, and you must tell work you won't be coming back for a while.'

'Thank God it hadn't spread. At least it seems quite small.' She tries to sound optimistic.

Paola decides we need to go out for tea. It's a welcome distraction. At four on a Monday afternoon I find myself in Patisserie Valerie on Marylebone High Street with her, Anat and Catherine. Paola's a freelance journalist for *Corriere della Sera*, the Italian daily, and this is usually her busiest time of day. Anat's an architect and Catherine's a management consultant, and they've both managed to escape from their offices.

'I'm afraid we've run out of scones,' our waitress says. 'You could have teacakes with clotted cream and jam instead. And it was Earl Grey you wanted?'

We don't talk much about what's happening, although of course that's the only reason we're here. To others, we must appear so carefree - four friends catching up in a smart café on a Monday afternoon.

It's four-thirty and I should be in the middle of a project meeting at Harrods. I've spent almost every Monday afternoon for the last six months there, sitting in an airless room above the store, the only woman among a sea of grey suits plus George.

After the first hour spent discussing details of things like mechanical extracts, hoardings and project programming, I would usually have to pinch myself under the table to stay alert.

In a bizarre way, it's actually quite nice to be here instead.

I return to hospital the next morning. Last week, it almost felt checking into a hotel. Today, I notice how ugly everything in the building is. The furniture in my room is covered with a skin of plastic veneer, made to look like wood. From the window I can see the bulky air conditioning units on the roof.

The surgeon comes in to tell me the biopsy for the new lump has come back negative.

'Don't you want to take it out anyway?'.

'No need at all.'

The trolley rattles in at noon and Paola, who's come by to visit, takes my mother out to lunch.

I wake up in the recovery room. The half-conscious woman next to me is whimpering and crying. I don't like being exposed to her pain.

'I want to go back to my room now,' I tell the nurse.

My mother and sister are waiting. As I'm rolled off the trolley and into bed, my sister stands next to me saying softly, 'You're so brave, so strong.' I don't feel brave or strong, but as if I've been catapulted into the air and have no control over either journey or destination.

My body is heavy, weighted. I spend the afternoon drifting in and out of sleep, waiting for the nausea to pass. Whenever I open my eyes I can see my mother and Tanya sitting by the window, talking very quietly. The minutes pass so slowly.

Paola comes back later, carrying a huge Gap bag.

'I've never spent so much money on clothes in one go. I just didn't know what to do with myself. So I bought the whole of

Gap.' She pulls out trousers, T-shirts, cardigans, a dress and Tanya brightens for the first time in days.

'Those linen trousers are fab. I'm going to have to get some.'

There's a clear plastic bottle half-filled with blood lying on the floor. It's connected to a thin tube and when I move there's a tug at my chest. I watch my blood drip slowly into this small vessel. Later, when the nurse comes in to empty it out I ask her to wrap it in a white pillowcase as I don't like seeing my body spill itself like this.

Tonight, I was supposed to be out. My boss Jamie recently completed a beautiful new house in Fitzrovia and the client's letting him have a huge party there. I was really looking forward to it. Jamie's invited his friends and lots of journalists and we were allowed to invite people, too. I lie in my hospital bed while only a few streets away, the life I should be living is taking place. Without me.

I pick up a message on my mobile from my friend Patrick the next morning. He called from the party at midnight, drunk, his voice only just audible above the thrash of music and conversation. I picture the concrete and timber living space, high as a church, filled with people drinking and dancing.

'What's going on, Bels? I asked Jamie where you were. All he'd say is you'd had to go to hospital. Fuck, I can't believe something bad's happening to you.'

The bottle hangs from my chest for two days. I carry it with me on my occasional journeys out of bed, feeling the warmth of my blood through its plastic skin.

An Australian nurse removes it on my last morning. She gives me a painkiller first but it still hurts. I look straight ahead as she changes my dressing. I haven't washed for two days and my body is both sour and antiseptic.

'You can have a bath now. Just make sure to keep your chest out of the water. I'll stay.'

Having unwrapped myself to strangers so often in the last few weeks, I've lost all sense of modesty. We chat as I sit in the bath.

'My grandmother had breast cancer when she was thirty. That was in Sydney over sixty years ago. Back then all they did was a mastectomy and no other treatment. She died last year aged ninety-three of something completely unrelated.'

It's the first story I've ever heard, which offers exactly the kind of ending I need. I'm so grateful to her for telling me. I hold it close, something to return to on dark days.

Back at my parents' house, I stare at my face in the bathroom mirror. It's different; thinner, paler and there are bruised rings under hollow eyes. I lift up my top. A clean white dressing has been taped over my breast. I move my fingers across it, trying to trace the topography of skin below, anticipating a fissure, that missing segment of the orange, but it still feels smooth.

I can only lift my left arm a few inches. Any higher and it's as if something inside's going to rip. It's because they had to cut through the nerve when they took the lymph nodes out. The hospital physiotherapist told me that if I do my exercises I should have the full range of movement back within a few weeks.

It's hard to wash my hair with one arm.

'I'll treat you to a blow dry,' my mother offers.

It's the first time I've been out and I'm shocked at how much strength I've lost. On the ten-minute walk to the salon in Primrose Hill, I have to stop three times. Only last week, my feet skimmed effortlessly across Manhattan.

My hair looks beautiful when it's finished. The curls are gone and it's straight and glossy.

A space opens up as the activity of the previous week subsides and I wait for my results. I spend a lot of time in bed, too exhausted to want to do anything. Here, I'm finally able to cry. Life has let me down in a way I never expected it to. I would worry about something happening to my parents, but it never really crossed my mind that I, so young and seemingly healthy, could get seriously ill. Now, I grieve for a future I may never have and for a present whose ordinariness now seems so precious. Just ten days ago, I lay in the sun on Union Square, drank cocktails in a bar high above Grand Central Station, and spent ages deliberating whether to buy my Seven jeans in dark or faded denim.

How long has the cancer been there? And why this has happened? I'm slim, I exercise, have a really good diet and don't drink much. Unlike the other girls at work who seemed to constantly have flu, migraines, or backaches, I almost never had to take a sick day.

My mother has, of course, voiced her own opinion.

'You rush around too much and your body's exhausted. And maybe there was something funny in those Chinese herbs you were taking for your eczema. God knows what they put in them.'

Some eczema and occasional asthma. That used to be the extent of my health problems.

I tell her she's being ridiculous, that you can't get cancer from being busy. And remind her that she got me into the Chinese herbs in the first place.

About eight years ago, my occasional mild eczema suddenly flared up. Steroid creams did little. Then my mother read about this Chinese woman in Chiswick in *The Evening Standard*. She barely spoke English and concocted brown paper packets filled with what looked like bits of tree bark and weird dried mushrooms. At home, I'd boil them up into foul smelling and tasting 'teas'. And soon my skin was completely clear again.

'It'll only be temporary and probably come back worse than before,' the GP warned.

But until six months ago, my skin stayed clear. This time it wasn't that bad but I went straight to the herbalist rather than even try steroids. And once again, it went away.

It's true I rushed around. But so does almost everyone I know. If you've got a demanding job, a busy social life and want to stay slim and fit, that's what you do. I'd go to the gym late in the evening after work, or early on Sunday mornings, often exhausted after a long day or a night out. I'd force myself through the tiredness barrier at the beginning and emerge high on adrenalin. I'd also recently started going to yoga before work on a Thursday, but my post class calm would usually dissolve almost instantly as, late for work, I'd stand on the platform at Chalk Farm cursing the infrequency of Bank trains. I was often tired. But in some ways that was good as it showed what a full life I had.

Apart from my immediate family, the only people who know are a few friends and Jamie, my boss. From my encounters of others with it, I've unfortunately been conditioned to view a cancer diagnosis as the beginning of the end. When only a couple of months ago Patrick told me his girlfriend Claudia was in Germany for the weekend to see her best friend as she'd just finished treatment for breast cancer, I thought, how awful to be dying so young.

I don't want people thinking the same about me. For the force of the word cancer to overshadow who I am, to have people whispering *Have you heard?... So young... Such a shame.* Nor to have to deal with the *How* are *yous?* from whoever I encounter.

It sounds silly, but having cancer is also at odds with the image I want to present to the world – of the healthy person who drinks organic carrot juice and green tea and does yoga.

So I decide I'm only going to share it with a few people. My friends can be roughly divided into three groups. The ones I see or speak to all the time and to whom I tell pretty much everything. They all already know. Then there are the ones to whom I'm still fairly close but have less regular contact with. I've told those who happened to call this week but I'm not sure I'll tell all of them. It doesn't seem necessary for people like Paul, who live abroad, and I won't see for a while, to know. The third group are the ones I usually only see with other people. We'll invite each other to dinners or parties but we wouldn't usually call for a chat or meet one on one. I'm not going to tell them.

I ask my mother not to tell her friends, apart from a couple that I'm also close to. Nor do I want all our relatives finding out.

'What about Ann?' Mum asks. Ann is eighty-four and, apart from my parents and sister, the only relative I have in London. Even though she's actually a distant cousin of my mother's, I call her my great aunt. She arrived in England alone in her early twenties, having lost her father and sister in a concentration camp, never married and has lived in the same small Kilburn flat for the last forty years. With no children of her own, she's always savoured every detail of my and Tanya's lives and is the closest thing I have left to a grandmother.

'I can't not tell her. Can you do it, though?'

Ann calls me a couple of days after my mother spoke to her.

'It's so unfair, so unfair,' she says in the German accent she's never lost, and sounding, for the first time ever, close to tears.

'It's going to be OK,' I hear myself say, even though I'm not at all sure that I believe those words myself.

I go to collect my results and hear what those who sliced, magnified and mapped both the edges and the centre of my tumour have to say. To them, every millimetre significant, helping create a forecast.

The nurse takes me into a narrow room next to the surgeon's office and tells me to sit down on the bed and undress to the waist. To quell the thoughts in my mind, I focus on the wall opposite. There's a long white work surface with drawers below. They're labelled with names such as *bowel instruments* and *suture cutters*. Above the work surface, an old sash window frame has been infilled with panels of mirror. It bothers me the way the top of the worksurface is higher than the bottom of the window and crashes awkwardly into it.

The surgeon comes in, strips off my dressing and tells me it all looks good. Only then do I dare look. In the mirror-window I see my left breast again for the first time. A raw pink line, dissected by two smaller ones, trails from nipple to armpit. I'm relieved to see it's still almost the same size as the right one and that, apart from the slightly raised ridge of the scar, the shape's smooth.

'I've even given you a bit of uplift. One day you might want to get the other one done to match.' I'm hoping the lightness in his tone means there's no more bad news to come.

In his office, he reads from the latest report.

'"Invasive *ductal carcinoma* measuring 12mm grades 2 and 3, and *ductal carcinoma insitu* measuring 7mm, grade 3. All nine of the lymph nodes sampled were clear. Oestrogen receptor status negative. *HER2* status negative." Do you realise you have a good prognosis?'

I'm not exactly clear what *good* means in this language? A brief period of remission, or something more enduring?

He's describing it as a 'little brush with cancer', making it sound like something which flew in randomly from nowhere and will soon be gone again.

'When can I go back to work?' I ask.

For the first time, I'm thinking about how I might still be able to hold on to my old life and how this may prove nothing more than a brief pause to its normal rhythm.

'Probably in a few weeks, but I'm not too sure. We've arranged you an appointment with the oncologist for tomorrow evening. He'll be able to give you a clearer idea.'

Oncologist. The word slashes through my train of thought. The ones who do chemotherapy.

'Why?' My voice rises. 'You've just told me what a good prognosis I have.'

'We send everyone who's been diagnosed. He may not even think you need any further treatment. He's a nice guy, went to the same university as you. I'm sure you'll get on.'

I don't give a shit he went to Cambridge. Why would that make me want to meet him?

6

It's seven-thirty in the evening. Unusually late for a doctor's appointment. A lot of people out there must have cancer. Harley Street's almost deserted; most of the parked cars are gone and the lights inside buildings are out.

The oncologist's offices are in a chocolate brown brick building, one of the few modern ones on this street. I leave behind the glow of the warm May evening and step into a cool, dark hallway. A metal lift silently ejects me into a long corridor lined with doors. One is ajar and has his name on it. I knock but no one answers, so I push it open. The waiting area is empty. Behind a second door, I can hear a muffled male voice.

I take a seat on a sofa placed behind a Japanese black latticework screen. All around me are artefacts and souvenirs from exotic places. There's a Buddha, a couple of African wooden masks and photographs of rainforests, temples and beaches.

This room is an ode to all the possibilities offered by life. Possibilities, which must surely contradict the contracting landscape of some who sit here and wait. Some, who have already perhaps taken their last holiday. I have always wanted to go to Japan.

Through the screen, I see the doctor's patient, a grey-haired woman wearing a gathered calf length skirt, shuffle out of the door, her head down. The doctor invites me in. He's in his early fifties, tall and slim with glasses, slightly receding hair and an authoritative voice.

He doesn't bother with the small talk routine. Briskly, he says, 'I've looked at your pathology. You'll need chemotherapy and radiotherapy.'

He may not even think you need any further treatment. I'd been trying to hang on to my surgeon's words. But now I'm being told about something called *FEC*, which I'll be given every three weeks. Six times in total. Followed by six weeks of daily radiotherapy.

'You should be finished by Christmas.'

Christmas. That's when we promised George the beauty spa will be open by.

'I was told I had a good prognosis. So why all this treatment?'

'You don't have an *especially* high risk of recurrence but you're not in the low risk category either. There are a couple of things I don't like about your tumour. There was vascular invasion, which means it had started to travel towards the lymph nodes. It's also mostly grade 3, the most aggressive. And oestrogen negative so you can't take *Tamoxifen*. Without treatment there's about a twenty-five percent risk of recurrence in the next five years. With it, we can reduce it to about sixteen percent.'

'What about the side effects?'

'They shouldn't be too bad. You might feel a bit off colour for a couple of days. You can lose your hair. But we always suggest patients wear an ice cap during treatment. It often helps you retain at least part of it. You've got so much. Even if you lost half, it wouldn't be that noticeable.'

Barely pausing for breath, he adds, 'I also need to tell you that you have about a thirty-five percent chance of losing your fertility. Permanently, that is.'

I gaze past him to the photograph on the mantelpiece of a blonde woman and three beautiful children swimming in an azure sea.

'So I'm more likely to lose my fertility from the treatment than I am to get cancer again if I didn't have it?'

'Don't worry too much about it,' he says glancing surreptitiously at his watch, thinking I haven't noticed. 'It's more important you don't get sick again.'

Such easy words to say. Has he ever actually thought about what it might be like for a young woman to lose her hair and her fertility? I swell with silent fury for the double blow of having been diagnosed and the threat of being left childless and ugly by its treatment. I swerve between images of dying young or being left barren, knowing my body has been a vessel for only the wrong kinds of growth.

The phone rings. From his response it's clear someone's asking what to do about a patient who's responding badly to treatment. He rattles off a long list of drugs and injections to be administered

'Don't worry, yours won't be as bad as this,' he mouths across the phone.

'So, when do you want to start?' he asks after he's put down the receiver.

Never.

'I'm supposed to be going on holiday to Spain in two weeks. I'm still hoping to go.'

'I certainly don't want you gallivanting around all summer. I'll agree to it if you come in and have your first session next week. You'll need to spend the night in hospital after so we can monitor you. We can organise it for Friday afternoons. You can then spend the weekend recovering and be back at work on Monday. It doesn't waste too much time that way.'

Slot it in between meetings and the pub. No big deal. Continue as normal. Pretend it's not really happening. Just don't let it rock the bloody boat.

As I listen to him, something inside me shifts: I can't do this and hold on to my old life at the same time.

I picture myself at my computer, feeling sick from chemo and plugging away at drawings while the phone rings continuously. George to say he's had yet another brainwave and the drawings I've just issued need to be revised. The builder to tell me there's yet another problem on site and I need to come down there straight away. Harrods management to complain the builders have damaged the Diana and Dodi fountain.

If I get better, I've got the rest of my life to work hard.

'So, can I book you in for Friday then?'

'I'll need to check my diary and get back to you.'

His eyebrows twitch in surprise.

As he's showing me out, his voice softens for the first time as he says, 'Unfortunately, we all have our cross to bear in life and may this be yours.'

I slam the front door when I arrive home.

'What did he say?' asks my mother. She wishes I'd let her come with me.

'Fucking wanker. With his perfect sorted out little life and family.'

How dare he tell me I need chemotherapy and could lose my fertility.

How dare he tell me it's no big deal.

How dare I get cancer.

For the first time, I'm sobbing uncontrollably. I kick the front door, bang my fists into furniture saying, 'It's not fair. It's not fair.' My parents watch, bewildered and helpless.

'I'm not having chemotherapy,' I shriek. 'I'd rather die than put that shit inside me.'

When I've calmed down, my father folds me in his arms and quietly holds me. His body feels solid and reassuring, smelling faintly of the aftershave I gave him last Christmas. My mother starts saying, 'But if that's what he says you need…'

He interrupts her. 'Not now. We can talk about this another time.'

Then I look at my watch.

'I'm really late for Ajay's dinner party.'

'You're in no state to be going out,' says my mother. 'Just stay with us. I've made plenty of food. I thought you might not feel like going.'

'I'm not letting this ruin my *entire* life.'

I wash my face and put on some makeup. It's after nine when I arrive so I make excuses about having been at work late. There are about fifteen people sitting in the living room eating the Indian feast Ajay's prepared. Smiling, I say hello to the ones I know and introduce myself to the unfamiliar faces, while inside I can still feel the rage pulsing in my chest.

At dessert I refuse the tiramisu. In the last few days, since reading a book about the influence of what we eat on breast cancer, I've stopped eating certain things, like dairy and sugar, and stopped drinking.

'Don't tell me you're on a diet,' Ajay, a natural beanpole, teases.

'I'm just doing a bit of a detox.'

'A friend did a month on raw food,' someone else says. 'She looked unbelievable after. Really glowing and thin and her eyes were enormous.'

'Sounds great.' How well would that work with chemotherapy?

Later, a Spanish guy notices my glass of water and asks why I'm not drinking.

'I'm just not in the mood tonight.' I decide not to mention the 'detox 'as he's quite good looking and I don't want him thinking I'm one of those girls who's constantly on a diet.

'It can't be much fun going out and not having a drink.' He puffs on his Marlboro. 'Can't I persuade you to have some wine?'

Could he be interested? And would he still be if I were bald? He doesn't ask for my number, so I never get the chance to find out.

When I leave, Ajay tells me I'm looking tired.

'Just a bit overworked at the moment.'

My friend Philippa's dad, who's a retired cancer surgeon, recommends another oncologist. She works at the Royal Free and was apparently one of his most talented students. Now she's a top consultant who actually specialises in breast cancer. Dr Alison Jones. A sensible, bluestocking kind of name. I picture squeaky shoes, thick ankles, glasses and mousey hair. Brainy, probably kind and well intentioned. Perhaps a little lacking in communication skills?

The grey concrete tower of the Royal Free rises like a factory over the surrounding Victorian villas and Hampstead parkland. I've been past it so many times, on my way to the Heath, but never had to go inside.

Dr Jones opens the door to her consulting room, blonde hair falling past her shoulders. She's around forty and is wearing a diaphanous skirt and a pair of pointed black knee length boots just like the ones I'd been looking for. I'm tempted to ask where she bought them.

I hoped she might suggest a less intense treatment regime. But her prescription is exactly the same as the male oncologist's.

'I'm not at all sure about chemotherapy. I hate taking medicine at the best of times and I'm really concerned about my fertility.'

'I do understand, but I think you need it. It is possible you could lose your fertility. But as you're only thirty-one, it's unlikely. There are also things which may be able to help you protect it.'

'I'm fully expecting you to come back in a few years with a photo to put in my baby book,' she adds.

The image of this book, filled with photos given by other women, who perhaps also thought they might never get that far, is enough to make me want to cry.

I ask about the hair loss and she repeats the other doctor's story about the ice cap, but she elaborates.

'Some women do lose their eyebrows and lashes as well. But you can always get the brows tattooed on and fake lashes. You'd be surprised at how glamorous you can look on chemo.'

It's so good to talk to another woman. To men, such concerns, in the face of cancer, probably seem trivial.

'I've booked to go on holiday to Spain at the end of next week. Can I still go?'

'I think it'll be good for you. As long as you start treatment as soon as you get back it won't make any difference to your prognosis. You could have it here, but as the insurance is paying, I'd suggest you go to the Harley Street Clinic. I work there too and it's more luxurious.'

She asks how much support I'm getting and whether I've got a partner. I tell her I'm close to my family and have wonderful friends but no boyfriend.

As I'm leaving she puts her hand on my shoulder and says, 'Hopefully I can cure you of cancer. I can't promise to find you a boyfriend, though.'

The other oncologist has left a harassed sounding message.

'Miss Chown, I've booked you in for Friday. I need you to get back to my secretary immediately to confirm.'

I don't call back that day and get another the following one.

'I'm very concerned I haven't heard from you. We must know if you're coming. There are limited spaces and I have a lot of patients on my list.'

I call the secretary straight back and tell her she can give the space to someone else on his long queue of desperate cancer patients, except of course I don't quite put it like that. I was hoping she'd ask why. But in a kind voice, she says, 'I just hope you find someone you feel comfortable with.'

I already have. I feel lucky, if you can use that word in this situation, to have found her, and to be in a position to be able to choose my doctor. Dark or faded denim? Sushi or Thai? Stay in or go to the gym? Those used to be the kinds choices I'd have to make.

Now, I need to decide whether or not to actually have this treatment.

7

I'm learning a new language. Words, which until recently meant nothing to me: *Cytotoxic. Vascular invasion. Adjuvant. Metastases. HER status. Oestrogen Negative.* These appear again and again on the computer screen. My brain is flooded with words and numbers. I am losing myself in a maze of facts.

What I do now understand is why the doctors want to give me this treatment. Although the cancer was cut away, what they don't know is whether undetectable traces of it escaped. To lie dormant in my body and perhaps become secondary tumours. The ones for which they can't offer a cure. The chemotherapy might kill off these random traces. But it might not. And they might not even be there, anyway.

I don't want to take these drugs. To risk not being able to have children and losing my hair. I don't normally even take aspirin. But I don't want to die, either. Vitamins, strange Chinese herbs, lots of fruit and vegetables. These have always served me well. Until now. But this is not some skin complaint.

The computer throws endless facts at me. Information that alternately soothes and terrifies. Often, the 'facts' contradict one another. Some say it's size that matters most. That's good. For others, it's the aggressiveness of the tumour. Not so good. Many state that clear lymph nodes mean it's less likely to recur, but others warn *it's no guarantee at all that the patient will have a positive outcome.* Some pay no attention to vascular invasion, others don't like it one little bit. My youth seems, for once, pretty much unanimously against me. Which feels horribly unfair.

Cancer alternative treatment. I punch these words into Google and over three million entries come up. 'Cures' for apparently even the most terminal of cases. Some weirder than others. Electro-chemical treatment kills off tumours by sticking needles into them A hyperthermia one heats the cancer up with infrared to get rid of it. Or you could try fasting. *The hungry body eats up the cancer.* Or even love - *the ultimate healer.*

Each regime asserts itself as The One that will cure you. If, of course, you follow it down to its last exacting detail. And price tag. Feeding people's fear is a profitable business. And there are few things more frightening than a cancer diagnosis. But how are you supposed to know which, if any, might work?

Conventional treatments are viewed with disdain. Chemotherapy, the greatest devil of all. Toxic. *You will only die more quickly.* The conventionals fight back. *Ours is the only proven way.*

Meanwhile, the alternatives bicker among themselves.

Eat only cooked food, state the macrobiotic crew.

Cooked is poison, damages the immune system, retaliate the raw foodists.

Aubergines, pineapples, avocadoes, tomatoes, tofu, brown rice, dairy are just a few of the things described as cure in some places, as curse in others.

Some warn of the dangers of plastic bottles and packaging, radiation on planes, dyes in clothes and even metal bed springs. If you want to, it's easy to start seeing the whole of the modern world as a giant cancer-making machine.

And so it goes.

Dotted all over, are also stories of miracle cures.

Fifteen glasses a day of fresh juice and multiple DIY coffee enemas stopped liver mets. Alive and well twenty years later.

But what of all the others who haven't made it to the front pages? Who are now dead despite having spent their last days sipping beetroot juice with a plastic hosepipe stuck up their backside?

Cancer, it seems, is unpredictable. Even the doctors don't know why some make it and others don't. I wish there were something I could do which would absolutely guarantee my survival. Instead, I'm lost in a shifting sea of unknowns.

Fear embeds itself into me, wedging itself into my stomach, my shoulders, my neck and jaw.

I can't help but be afraid of not being able to complete my life, and of losing control of my body and my appearance. I don't want to ever be a hairless, pale, sick-looking person, visibly ebbing away. To have the shadow of death tattooed on me.

I know I'll have to die one day. But I always assumed it would take place in a future too distant to even imagine. Although the days and weeks would always drain away too quickly, time also seemed infinite. I couldn't imagine it might ever stop coming.

A couple of months ago, Ioana sent me an email with a link to a questionnaire that claimed it could determine your longevity. Mine came out at ninety-three. I wrote back saying, *I've got forever. Just hope you'll be around to share it with me.*

Suddenly, I'm seeing decay everywhere. It's early summer and the flowers are in full bloom but I see how each day brings them closer to autumn. I notice the erosion on the brick and stone facades of the buildings I pass. I look at little children in the park and fast-forward to them as old men and women.

I keep all these thoughts private. No one likes talking about death, especially with someone who has cancer.

How can I now trust my body? I inhabit only its surface. Its interior, separated by a few millimetres of skin, is so close and yet so far.

What secrets could hide in the uncharted territories beneath skin? Could my occasional stomach aches be something sinister? And what of all the other places, the ones of which I know nothing, can feel nothing?

My imagination takes over. It designs a new interior behind these walls of skin, one where tumours press against and dislodge the existing architecture of bones, or infill its cavities. It's a hidden, silent landscape, unregistered on the surface contours of my body.

I know I shouldn't be having these thoughts. But something's taken over, sending my mind into a frenzied tailspin. I never used to be a hypochondriac. And I'm feeling guilty for not being able to stop the thoughts. *The mind heals the body. Positive thinking can cure cancer,* the alternatives preach.

Instead, I become intimate with skin. My hands constantly trace its surface, fingers stroking breasts or digging deep into the crevices of armpit, groin and neck. Discovering for the first time the subtle web of bumps and ridges of tissue, glands and muscle, which lie beneath skin. Unsure now of what's normal and what's not.

When I visit Aunt Ann for tea, as I've now started to sometimes do mid-week, she comments on how I keep stroking my neck. I wasn't even aware how habitual it had become.

'One of my neighbours in the building had breast cancer,' she says, as we sit on her ancient brown sofa, drinking tea out of the blue and white cups patterned with birds and flowers.

'Whenever I'd see her in the garden from my window she'd be doing exactly the same as you. Now I understand why.'

I even make an appointment to see my GP to discuss my concerns. I've placed bits of masking tape on the raised bumps

I've felt in my neck and groin so he can actually find them - so obvious are they.

'We all have a necklace of lymph glands running around our neck,' he tells me. 'It's completely normal for them to sometimes be slightly raised.'

I ask if it's possible to have a whole-body scan carried out, telling him how the initial misdiagnosis has amplified my fear.

'But as you know, your scans showed absolutely no evidence of secondary spread.'

'What if I have another primary somewhere completely unrelated? How can I be sure the headache I had last week isn't a brain tumour?'

'It was probably triggered by the stress of what you've been going through. Having another primary is very, very unlikely.'

'But so was getting breast cancer in the first place,' I retort.

'It was, and you've been really unlucky. It's completely normal to be scared. I'm confident there's nothing else going on, though.'

Perhaps fear is also my protector. If I were to let go of it and relax, just like I did before the first operation, something bad might happen again.

I need to make a decision about this chemotherapy. If I could be guaranteed it would prevent the cancer from ever coming back and wouldn't make me infertile, I'd have it like a shot, hair loss and all. But what I'm battling with are the statistics. Twenty-five percent likely to come back without it. Sixteen percent likely with it. And one third my age will lose their fertility. Is it really worth it for a nine percent improvement on the odds?

My parents definitely think so. So does my sister, who dislikes taking medicine as much as I do. And added to the weight of their voices is my own: imagine if you didn't and then it came back and you knew you hadn't done everything you could have.

'No alcohol, dairy or sugar,' says the glamorous blonde doctor in her New Cavendish Street consulting room. 'You'll also need to cut out red meat, coffee and refined carbs. And of course, all processed and fast food.'

I've come to get advice on what, or rather what not, to eat. A qualified GP, who now prefers to treat her patients holistically, she's apparently good with cancer.

What I can have are fruit and vegetables, wholegrains, pulses, tofu, some fish and chicken. All preferably organic. It sounds a lot more sensible than some of the things I read on the Web. *Eat only purple foods. It is a healing colour.*

Pinned to the wall behind her desk, is a photo of Geri Halliwell in her super skinny days. It's signed, *To the most gorgeous doc in the world.* Maybe I'll also end up that thin, I think, hopefully.

She writes out a list of supplements and suggests I come back for some vitamin infusions, supposed to be good for the cancer and also for alleviating some of the toxicity of the chemotherapy drugs.

'Have some massages, do gentle yoga and get plenty of rest and fresh air,' she adds. This part sounds good.

'How can you be sure this diet's going to make any difference?' my mother asks, watching me juice fennel, celery, spinach and lemon into an emerald liquid, a couple of mornings later. 'You always ate healthily. So maybe it's nothing to do with that.'

I'm surprised by her scepticism. When we were growing up, fizzy drinks and biscuits were banned from our house. Mum would sometimes cook brown rice, which in those days Tanya and I loathed, and she gave us tofu years before it became a fashionable health food. At our friends' houses we'd gorge on forbidden Jaffa Cakes, Clubs and Wagon Wheels. We'd sneak out to the newsagents to spend our pocket money on Space Dust, which crackled in our mouths, 1p cola bottles, Curly Wurlys, and lemon sherbets, and have midnight feasts in our bedroom. But as adults, we've both pretty much reverted back to the healthy habits she'd tried to instil in us all those years ago.

'You've already lost weight,' she says and I then realise the real reason for her concern. 'It's not healthy to be too thin. Especially now when you need all your strength.'

I'm slim, but I've certainly never been too thin. I have fantasised about being a size eight rather than a ten but it would take too much effort and I enjoy food too much. I'm actually pleased at how the stress of the last few weeks has made the weight fall so effortlessly off me. I haven't even had to go to the gym. I also read somewhere that chemotherapy can make you put on weight, due to the steroids you have to take with it. So, I'm delighted to be starting this diet. But, of course, I don't mention this to my mother.

I quite like all the foods the doctor's told me I can eat. They're not even that dissimilar to what I ate before. What's harder is giving up what I'm not supposed to have: a glass of wine with a meal, a cappuccino, grilled halloumi cheese, chocolate brownies. But I'm surprised by how much willpower I suddenly develop. In the past, when I'd occasionally tried a detox type diet, to lose a bit of weight or feel more energetic, I normally gave up after a couple of days.

What I do miss is eating for pleasure, enjoying food just for its flavour and texture. Now I read nutrition books to find out which ones have the highest level of vitamins and examine labels in Fresh & Wild and Waitrose to check everything's free from illegal ingredients and additives. Eating has become a mechanical act.

Having children's not something I've thought that much about. Until now. I've always wanted them, in the abstract at least, but meeting the right man was my first priority.

My mother gave birth to me at thirty-nine and my sister at forty-one, both of us easily conceived, at a time when it was rare to have your first child so late. So perhaps that's why I always felt as if I had a bit of time. I've got single friends my age who've already been to the doctor to find out about freezing their eggs. But now the thought of going through treatment to perhaps discover afterwards that this particular door has slammed shut is devastating.

The gynaecologist runs through the options available to try and protect my fertility.

Freezing my eggs. Without a partner to fertilise them, it has a very low success rate.

Freezing a slice of ovarian tissue. A technique only in its pioneer stages and no-one knows if it'll even work.

Taking a hormone suppressor which temporarily shuts down the ovaries and may protect the eggs from being damaged.

For the first two procedures, I'd need a general anaesthetic. To take the drugs I'd need to be at a certain point in my cycle and then they'd need time to kick in before I could start chemotherapy. We work out this would mean delaying it for an additional three weeks.

'It's not worth the risk, especially when it might not even work,' he advises.

I discuss it with my mother, going round in circles. Convinced one minute that I have to do anything I can, even if it might not work and involves yet another operation. Thinking the next that it's mad to put myself through something so unlikely to work.

'Don't do anything,' is her advice. 'My gut feeling is you'll be OK as you are. Sometimes in life you just have to allow what will be to be.'

It's frightening leaving things to chance. But, as I'm starting to realise, it's a world full of unknowns.

8

I haven't been at work for over a month. As I shed my old life, initiation into my new one takes on its own rhythm. Occasionally I glimpse myself, as if in a mirror, and can't believe this is really happening.

Some days my diary looks as if it belongs to a lady who lunches:*10am yoga, 1pm lunch with Paola, 4pm acupuncture.* Others, it does not: *11am, 81 Harley Street.* My Harley Street appointment is not for a shot of Botox.

I go there for the first time a couple of days before I leave for Spain. One of the chemotherapy nurses wants to meet me and run through the treatment.

The exterior of number eighty-one is indistinguishable from the other buildings on the street, apart from a discrete brass plaque by the door engraved with *Oncology Day Care Unit.* Flanking the steps are two tall black metal posts, which probably once held street lamps. Their ends are curved into spiral shapes, which for some reason look menacing.

A girl my age, with a shiny bald head, is standing outside the building laughing and chatting with two friends. What does she think she's got to be happy about walking around with cancer and no hair? I move quickly past her and go up the stone steps, hesitating before I push open the heavy wooden entrance door.

I'm in a hallway with a polished black and white diamond patterned floor leading to a mahogany desk. A receptionist appears and directs me into the waiting room where I know I will have to encounter other people with cancer.

It's a large room with several sofas and armchairs, but it's so full I have to search for a seat. I find an empty one underneath a poster that tells us to eat five portions of fruit and vegetables a day. It's illustrated with a picture of an apple, a tin of peaches and a bottle of tomato ketchup. I pick up *The Independent* from a coffee table and pretend to read while surreptitiously checking everyone else out, looking for traces of cancer in faces and scalps, bodies and gestures. I sense other people's eyes on me. Most are at least a couple of decades older.

I seek evidence of the common ground that has brought us to this room. But I'm surprised to find almost nothing. There are several couples waiting but, apart from an occasional bare scalp, it's often hard to tell which of the two is here for treatment.

Natasha, the chemotherapy nurse, leads me up an ornate, curved period staircase framed by an oval skylight to a consultation room on the second floor. She hands me three sheets of typed paper. They are headed *Fluorouracil*/Clear *Epirubicin*/Red and *Cyclophosphamide*/Clear. Three drugs, together known as *FEC*. Each page has a list of all their possible side effects. There are at least ten per sheet. Aside from those I've already been warned about they also include *cardiotoxic toxicity* (heart problems) and *haemorrhagic cystitis* (inflammation and bleeding of the bladder).

'Do people really get these?' I'm surprised no-one's mentioned them before.

'They're extremely rare. But it's not uncommon to get things like a sore mouth, inflamed veins, eye infections and a lowered blood count.'

Natasha looks at my shoulder length hair, which I've been trying to grow for the past year.

'Now, I know Dr Jones mentioned the ice cap. It's up to you whether you want it. Some people can't tolerate having what can feel like a block of ice pressed on their head. If you do, you'll need a haircut. It's not effective with long hair.'

'How short?'

She points to my jaw-line, 'At least that short.' Over a year's worth of growth.

Before I leave, she gives me two booklets. One is called *The Harley Street Oncology Unit*. Its glossy royal blue cover has a photograph of the building's façade, an ornamental balcony above an elegant fan-lit door, set within a rusticated stonework surround. It could almost be the brochure for a boutique city hotel. Inside, a picture of the chemotherapy room shows patients sitting in armchairs smiling. The other, *The Cancer Guide*, is subtitled *It's all about helping you to live with it*. The images in it are of happy looking people - one couple are dancing, another is out shopping. There are children feeding the ducks and a man smiles from his chopping board as he slices an orange. Even cancer, it seems, has had a PR makeover.

I'm selling my flat. I'd been vaguely thinking of moving from South Hampstead and buying in Camden, Primrose Hill or Belsize Park. The agents came by the week before I found the lump and I was shocked to find the value had doubled since I'd bought it less than four years ago. They loved the high ceilings, big windows and clean lines.

'So many people on our books would buy this tomorrow,' they said, enticingly.

I said I wasn't sure I was ready to sell, that I needed to first look around the areas I was interested in and check what was available at my budget. Every few days they'd call to ask whether I'd decided, dangling tantalising descriptions of first-time cash buyers apparently desperate for a flat just like mine in front of me. At first, I said no. But once I'd decided to have chemotherapy, I told them to put it on.

I've been at my parents' for over a month. They've told me I can stay as long as I want. I've realised I don't actually want to live alone while I'm having treatment. As I'm no longer earning, I couldn't afford to pay the mortgage anyway. I appreciate having them and all their little routines around me. My dad making constant pots of Darjeeling at the weekend, the sounds of *Radio Three* coming out of his study. My mum gardening and cooking or telling me and Dad off for leaving the kitchen in a mess or spilling tea on the carpet.

To my surprise, the agents live up to their promises. Within a week a buyer, first time, cash and asking price, is found. The day before we leave for Spain, I accept the offer.

I'm going to Spain to do a yoga holiday.

'Lots of yoga, delicious food and a beautiful setting - it sounds perfect,' said Paola when we saw the flyer months earlier. 'Just think how toned and thin we'll look when we get back.'

'Shouldn't you just be getting on with treatment?' my mother said when I tell her I'm still going. But with months of it to come and a future that now feels precarious, I want a pause.

Paola and I started yoga last year, after I saw an article in a magazine about Bikram yoga, practised in a room heated to over 100 degrees Fahrenheit. It was supposed to be a fast route to slim thighs and a detoxed body.

We found Bikram's Yoga College of India at the top of three flights of stairs behind a battered metal door on a parade of shops in Kentish Town. The yoga room was extremely hot and smelt of the disinfectant being pumped through the heating system. Despite this, stale feet air rose up from the grey carpet floor. An hour and a half later we left exhilarated and dripping with sweat. I texted Paola the next day, *Can hardly walk! Hope u up for it again x.*

For months, we went to Kentish Town almost every Tuesday evening and I watched my thighs tighten and my friendship with Paola deepen. We were friends at school, but until about eighteen months ago were in touch only occasionally. Then I started dating someone who happened to be a friend of hers from university. I called her to tell her about the coincidence. The guy only lasted a few months but ever since, Paola and I have become increasingly close.

I told Tanya, who'd also recently got into yoga, to try a Bikram class.

'That place is a dump,' she said after. 'It was so hot I nearly passed out and had to leave the room.'

I pictured my lily-skinned, long-limbed sister sitting alone on the bench in the tiny changing room while everyone else grunted and sweated their way through the requisite twenty-six postures.

'Anyway, I've started going to this amazing place in Primrose Hill called Triyoga,' she continued. 'You should try it.'

One rainy Monday evening in late October, we found ourselves in a high-ceilinged candlelit room with huge windows and white walls and floors.

'That's Simon,' whispered Tanya, pointing to a silver-haired man in his forties lighting incense sticks and wearing a T-shirt saying *Om Shanti*. 'He's meant to be one of the best teachers in London.'

The class was packed, mostly with attractive women in their twenties and thirties, plus a few men.

Simon guided us through the poses in a smooth deep voice. At Bikram, we'd finish them and leave the room immediately, all wired and sweaty. In contrast, Simon slowly wound down the class, before having us lie on the floor with our eyes closed for almost ten minutes in what he called *Savasana* or Corpse Pose, describing it as, 'The most important part of the yoga practise, when your body can really soak up the benefits of all the work you've done.'

'I feel completely blissed out,' I told Paola after.

'Me too. I don't miss that grey carpet either.'

We never went back to Kentish Town. Throughout the autumn and into the following spring, Simon's Monday evening class became our after-work routine. I'd usually get there tired after an afternoon stuck in the windowless room at the top of Harrods. It was always a relief to arrive in this warm white space overlooking the back gardens of Primrose Hill and to move and stretch my body, and quieten my mind. My friend Anat started coming too and afterwards the three of us would often go for dinner at Manna, the vegetarian restaurant opposite. I loved those evenings. Despite whatever had gone on at work, I'd feel drawn into a cosy, protected enclave. It was at Manna, one Monday night in April, when I mentioned to them that I needed to have a small operation. I was surprised by how concerned they seemed.

Our flight is delayed so we're the last of the group to arrive in Malaga where the bus is waiting to take us up to the hills. Everyone else looks annoyed at having had to wait an extra two hours. In silence, we drive along the coast past all the Costa del Sol holiday resorts before turning inland, where the land begins to rise and swell. It's already dusk and from the window I follow the yellow pin pricks of car lights curving down the opposite side of the road.

It's dark when we arrive. The air smells of rosemary and orange. Just breathing in its quiet scent is a release. The retreat's being held in a converted stone farmhouse set among olive groves and almond trees. There are twenty of us plus Simon. Nineteen women and one man who's been brought by his wife.

Over dinner, we start getting to know one another. When I talk, I erase the last month of my life and instead tell them about the work I'm doing for Harrods and my flat in South Hampstead.

We start yoga at seven the next morning, gathering on the large roof terrace wrapped in sweaters and surrounded by the bruised purple masses of the still dark mountains. Slowly, we unfurl our bodies from the heaviness of sleep as the rising sun gradually warms our skin. I've done a few yoga classes since the surgery but I'm stiffer and weaker than usual. And I still can't lift my left arm all the way up.

After just a couple of days I'm so much calmer. In this beautiful remote setting where life is pared down to yoga, rest, food and conversation, I feel removed from the past weeks in London.

Gradually, I'm returning to the body I had left behind. The palpable one, where skin stretches and folds, bones rotate and muscles lengthen and contract. The one which enjoys the touch of sunlight and sweat across its surface. The one that had been overspread by fear, generated by something weighing only a few grams.

Between classes, we spend lots of time sitting by the pool, or under the trees in the orchard. Some of the women sunbathe topless. I couldn't find a bikini that completely hid my scar so I usually keep my T-shirt on. One morning, I overhear a blonde woman on the next sun lounger telling a new friend in a low voice about her recent boob job. I glance over. She's topless but I can't see any evidence of a scar, just big, beautiful tanned breasts. I'll never be comfortable doing that again, I think, enviously.

In the late afternoons, as the heat starts to slacken, there's a second yoga class. It's less energetic than the morning one, but the postures are often intense. Simon gets us to hold seated poses like forward bends and hip openers for several minutes at a time. It's meant to open up the connective tissue between joints and work into the areas we tend to feel tight in. I'm usually ready to come out of the shapes long before he tells us to.

'Focus on your breath,' he instructs us. 'Draw each one right in to the areas where you feel the strongest sensations. Stay present with them, take it breath by breath, moment by moment.'

Mentally breaking it down as he suggests does make it more bearable. I think of the months of treatment ahead and remind myself to try and do the same thing.

After dinner, we carry cushions and blankets up to the roof terrace and sprawl out. As the week goes by, people's stories spill out. I hear about the sadness of failed attempts at IVF, a recent divorce, ill parents. Soaking up everyone else's stories while hiding my own makes me feel a bit of a fraud. But I just want to try and forget about cancer as much as possible this week.

The only person I share it with is a man who gives me a shiatsu massage one afternoon.

'I'd really recommend you have some counselling while you're going through this,' he advises. 'It's very difficult to talk honestly about how you're feeling to those close to you. You don't want to upset them and they just want to be reassured you're OK.'

He's absolutely right. I would never share my fears about dying with my family, and not even with the majority of my friends.

Most of us on the holiday are in our thirties but there's a group of four women who are a bit older. They all seem to know each other from before and pretty much keep to themselves. Paola takes me aside one morning.

'I was sitting near them at breakfast today and couldn't help overhearing their conversation. Turns out that Jo, you know the one who's a yoga teacher, had breast cancer. She recently finished chemo. Not that you'd guess.'

'But she's even still got hair,' I say, excitedly.

'Let's sit near them when we go on the picnic later and see if we can find out anything else.'

When we arrive at the riverbank for the picnic, Paola and I wait for them to sit down and position ourselves on the nearest rock and eat our lunch in silence. We don't find out much except that she had a mastectomy and she didn't like drinking while she was on chemo as it made her feel sick.

'I'll try and get her into conversation sometime and get some more information for you,' offers Paola, ever the journalist.

The only other thing she discovers is that she did wear an ice cap and did lose part of her hair but managed to cover up the bald patch with the rest. I hardly speak to her all week but my eyes constantly follow her around. Is this how I will be after?

The week passes too quickly. I want these summer days to never end, to remain forever suspended in their bloom. But it's almost time to go home.

On our last evening, we all go out for dinner. Everyone apart from me, who was relieved at having been able to do so, is tired of having eaten such wholesome vegetarian food all week. Our table is a long line of lamb carcasses.

The girl on my right starts telling me about her chronic repetitive strain injury and how no one understands how miserable it is living with it. 'It's so unfair,' she says. 'If I had cancer everyone would give me lots of sympathy. Because it's RSI no-one takes it seriously.'

Want to swap, I feel like asking. Instead I say, 'I can imagine it can't be much fun. But I guess the difference is you can actually die from cancer. I haven't yet heard of anyone dying of RSI.'

It's early evening and we're flying north along the east coast of Spain, against the backdrop of a sinking sun. The thin sliver of a new moon floats high in the sky. Beneath it, the furious glow of the sun bleeds across the horizon. I have never seen a sunset so intense. It's as if the energy of the whole world were contained within that band of orange sky.

These days I search for meaning in places where I used to find none. The sun seems to be staring at me, throwing me its light and energy and following me as we fly. It's telling you not to despair, that it's all going to be OK in the end, I try to persuade myself.

9

Chemotherapy begins in four days. I need to get a haircut.

I don't want to go to my regular salon in Primrose Hill and have to explain why I've suddenly decided to cut off the hair they know I've been growing for months. I book an appointment at a place I find online, on Kensington High Street and supposed to specialise in short hair. When I call up, the receptionist recommends Omar. 'He's great with really close cuts.'

It's a dense afternoon. One of those days when the heat forces everything to move in slow motion. Exhaust fumes and dust hang in the air.

There are no other customers in the salon. Stylists sit around aimlessly. A young Middle Eastern man looks up when I walk in. I tell him I want a completely new cropped look. But today short is not what Omar wants to be doing.

'Cutting it all off would only emphasise its thickness and curliness. It's a good length so why don't we just reshape it.'

Unfortunately, I'm not here for aesthetics.

'Please just make it short.'

Damp lengths of my hair lie on the salon floor as Omar makes small talk.

'What do you do?'

'Architecture.'

'Busy at the moment then?'

'Yeah, pretty busy, working quite hard.'

'Anything special planned over the next few days?'

'Just catching up with friends, you know the usual.'

I gaze at my changing self in the mirror and remember the last time I had my hair cut. It was at Harrods, exactly eight weeks ago, and the day before my first appointment with the surgeon.

'Look at you,' George said afterwards. 'None of the boys in the office will be able to keep their hands off you.'

When Omar has finished, I have a very short, wispy bob.

'What you do think?' He swirls me through a 360-degree view with his hand-held mirror.

I hate it.

'It's lovely. Thank you.'

'Good. Come back in about six weeks for a trim.'

The day before chemotherapy begins, I go to the Sam Taylor Wood exhibition at the Hayward Gallery. I go to seek evidence of hope. She had colon cancer in 1997, at thirty, followed by breast cancer in 1999. I read about it in a magazine months ago, in the days when cancer happened to other people.

I stand alone in one of the cool concrete recesses of the gallery and cry silent tears as I watch a video of a man dancing in slow motion to Samuel Barber's Adagio for Strings. Alone in his bedroom, his naked body stretches into space, its fragile form tracing his hopes, dreams and fears.

The most beautiful piece in the exhibition is a photograph of a tree in a field, entitled *Self Portrait as a Tree*. The tree is bathed in light while the surrounding landscape is dark and stormy. I stare at it for several minutes. In the bookshop, I browse the exhibition catalogue and discover it was the only piece of work she made while she was having chemotherapy for breast cancer.

On the eve of midsummer's day, I have my first session of chemotherapy. Dr Jones and her nurses tried to reassure me *it's not like in the old days*, but the only images I hold are from films and books. Soon after my diagnosis, one of my friends said to me, 'Well, at least you won't have to have chemotherapy, will you?' Months earlier, she told me about the night she spent in a hospital ward with several women who were being treated for breast cancer.

'It was just so upsetting to see all these young women who had no hair and were so sick,' I remember her saying.

The consultants' waiting room at the oncology unit is designed to try and make you feel at ease. Its mint green walls are washed with soft uplighting and hung with pastel watercolours of landscapes. A vase filled with fake flowers has been placed in the hearth. There is one other woman waiting. She has a bandanna tied around her head.

'Your hair's not as short as I'd have liked,' announces Dr Jones.

I fire questions at her. How exactly will I feel? Will I be sick? How long will it last? She smiles.

'You'll probably feel a little off colour tomorrow, as if you had a hangover, or were coming down with flu. By Saturday you should be fine. I suggest you plan something nice. Like a bit of shopping and lunch with a friend at Harvey Nichols. You could also pop over the road for a massage at the Mandarin Hotel.'

George took me round the Mandarin when we were coming up with ideas for Harrods. I was shocked to find a massage cost £150.

The chemotherapy room occupies the entire first floor of the building. Once, it must have been someone's drawing room. It has four-metre high ceilings and tall skinny sash windows overlooking Harley Street. The city is filtered out by sheer white curtains. About fifteen large armchairs with built in footrests are scattered around the room. It reminds me of the lounge of a gentleman's club, except cigars and whiskey are replaced by drip stands and plastic bags of jewel-coloured liquids, waitresses by nurses in blue uniforms. Most of the armchairs' occupants appear at ease. They read glossy magazines, chat to friends, eat egg sandwiches and drink tea as the drugs drip-drip into them.

I take a seat in the corner. My mother joins me. It's the first time she's been inside this building. What must this feel like for her? She wears a bright smile. She still seems to smile a lot these days and is always telling me, 'Don't worry, it's all going to be fine in the end.'

I haven't let her to come to any of my appointments with the doctors. I didn't want her to embarrass me by asking too many questions, to have her make me feel like a child again. But today I need her.

An Irish nurse, Breda, gives me my treatment. It has a precise choreography.

Remove first ice cap from freezer, place on patient's head, set timer for thirty minutes.

Bright blue nylon and looks like a cross between a tea cosy and a swimming cap. Burning cold neck, ears, forehead.

Bleep bleep bleep.

Remove second ice cap from freezer, place on head, set timer for thirty minutes. Place heated pads on right arm to keep veins warm.

A dull pain has spread across my head and neck.

Tap, tap, tap for a vein and insert canula.

It won't go in. She tells me I'm too tense. 'Try and just relax.'

Administer anti-emetic injection.

As she warned me, it feels as if a hedgehog has been let loose inside my knickers.

Inject two syringes of Ebiprubicin.

Beautiful red liquid, the colour of rubies and sunsets bleeding into my veins, drowning me in a red sea.

Bleep bleep beep.

Remove third ice cap from freezer, place on head, set timer for thirty minutes.

Spears of ice are stabbing my head, my neck, my sinuses. It's like the time I ate too much wasabi with my sushi by mistake. All I can hear is the tick-tock of the timer muffled from behind a layer of ice. Every half hour seems longer than the last.

Inject one syringe of Fluorouracil.

Breda's trying to chat to me, take my mind off it all. She's so impressed when I tell her I'm an architect. Actually, I'm not really much of an anything these days.

Infuse one bag of Cyclophosphamide.

Bleep beep bleep.

'Nearly done love, no more ice caps, we'll just flush you out now.'

Infuse one bag of water.

Dripping so slowly.

When I stand up, I feel weak but not sick. Breda hands me a white paper bag. Inside, there are three different types of anti-sickness tablets, steroids, a bottle of mouthwash and a sheet of complex instructions on when to take each one. I use the toilet and my urine is bright red and smells of chemicals.

I step back out into the summer day. It's early afternoon and the sun is high in the sky. My mother wants me to go home and rest but I insist she takes me shopping at Fresh & Wild in Camden. At home, I make brown rice and a vegetable juice and take the anti-sickness tablets as instructed. I spend the rest of the afternoon lying in the garden, distractedly leafing through *Marie Claire* and *Elle Decoration*. By early evening I'm nauseous. Around nine I start to vomit.

My knees slam against the bathroom tiles, my arms grasp the cold white gleam of the toilet bowl. When I'm empty again there's a brief sweetness, a lull. I sink into the softness of my mattress and fall asleep for a few minutes before the sickness swells in my throat again. Each time I think will be the last. But the sickness is like the wave of an ocean, returning again and again to its shore. By 3 a.m, I have vomited over twenty times. I recall the words I read in one of my alternative cancer books:

Try and visualise the chemotherapy as a beautiful healing energy entering your body.

Beauty can take many forms, but not this.

I begin to think the drugs have poisoned me. I call the oncology unit. A German nurse answers, cool and efficient.

'No, you are most definitely not dying. This is quite normal. You should come here and collect some suppositories. This may help you.'

'How can I come in the middle of the night in this state? Could you send them in a cab?'

'I am afraid we are not able to do this.'

When daylight brushes my window, I finally fall asleep. For the next two days, my world is limited to the shadowy confines of my room, curtains drawn tight to obliterate the intensity of the summer days. I am swathed in the residues of the chemotherapy. I can smell its chemicals rising from my pores, infusing my sheets, pillow and pyjamas. When I breathe, the air is like acid searing my nostrils. I imagine myself trapped in a smoke-filled landscape, burning in a forest fire. I am repulsed by the familiar; bright sunlight, my mother's perfume, the smell of dinner being prepared in the kitchen.

The steroids I was told to take make me edgy and restless so despite my exhaustion I don't sleep much. I have nothing to distract me. I'm not used to lying in bed for long periods of time and having such an intimate connection with my body's discomfort.

When I do start to eat again, I crave only soft protective foods, in small quantities. Spaghetti with butter, cheese on toast, mashed potatoes, rice pudding. The foods of my childhood, from a time when life was still simple.

June 26th is my thirty-second birthday. My star sign, Cancer. It's six days after chemotherapy and I am still fragile. My body feels all silted up and my skin's breaking out.

'How do you want to celebrate?' my mother asked a couple of days earlier.

'I'm not that bothered.'

I had a party for my last birthday. Around thirty people came over to my flat and we shared food, wine, conversation and music until the early hours.

'Your friends have been so supportive. I think it'd be nice to have them over. I'm happy to cook.'

'That's really sweet.' I wish I could feel more enthusiastic.

On my birthday, I meet up with Ayala and her three-year-old son JJ on top of Primrose Hill. She's bought us lunch from Sesame, the local health food store.

'I've got brown rice salad with vegetables, some things stuffed with spinach and tofu, and this mushroom, tahini and walnut strudel. All dairy free.'

I try and eat but end up giving most of it to JJ. He eats some, squashes the rest into little balls and tosses it at the birds.

'I'm sorry, but I'm allergic to anything remotely healthy. I've completely ditched my diet for now.'

Yesterday, I even persuaded my mother to drive me all the way to Camisa, the Italian deli on Old Compton Street, just to buy tortelloni. I haven't had it in years. It used to be one of my favourite treats, the big billowy cushions of pasta filled with delicate spinach and ricotta and covered in melted butter and parmesan. She got frustrated while we were stuck in traffic on Regent Street for almost half an hour. But later, when she saw me eating a big plate of pasta, she said, 'I'm so glad you're eating properly again.'

'I was exactly the same for a while during my pregnancy,' says Ayala. 'I felt so sick every time I tried to eat stuff like broccoli. It's funny how your body can react so strongly against things it normally likes.'

In her calm, thoughtful way, Ayala starts asking exactly how I'm feeling about everything. She's one of those rare people who's completely unafraid of delving into the places others find awkward. I tell her about the chemo, and how scared and isolated I often feel. While I talk, her large, soft brown eyes keep looking right into mine.

Although I refuse even to tell most people I have cancer, with those who do know, I long to talk openly. It's just sometimes I'm not sure how much others want to know.

JJ pretends to hide in the long swathes of uncut grass near where we're sitting. Every few minutes he runs back to us shrieking and giggling, jumping into our laps and playing with Ayala's long dark-blonde hair, blissfully unaware of our conversation. I look at him and can't help thinking about what I may never have.

In the evening, about ten friends come over. Their presents are even more generous than usual and include a cream cashmere pashmina, a voucher for a treatment at a spa in South Kensington and a box of Dr Hauschka products. I was slightly dreading the evening because of the bittersweetness of celebrating so soon after my diagnosis. At the beginning, as we stand in the garden with our drinks, I sense a slight awkwardness. People seem unsure about how much they should or shouldn't be asking. But soon we all relax. My mother puts out big bowls of chicken, couscous and roast vegetables and as we sit down to eat, laughing and gossiping, it's just like normal again.

As a birthday treat, my parents take me to the Royal Opera House to see Tchaikovsky's *The Queen of Spades*. A singer called Susan Chilcott is making her Covent Garden debut in the lead role. Less than a year ago, at thirty-eight, she was diagnosed with breast cancer. In a recent interview in *The Evening Standard*, which my mother cut out for me, she said her prognosis was good and she felt well.

On stage, a beautiful woman sings Tchaikovsky's ethereal music and fills me with me hope. What I can't know now is that in a year she will be dead.

A couple of days later, I go for my first vitamin infusion.

'There's someone here I want you to meet,' says the glamorous blonde doctor when I arrive. 'Her name's Patricia. She's an art historian who's had secondary breast cancer in her bones for the past couple of years. I've been giving her regular infusions. She's doing really well.'

I don't particularly want to meet someone whose breast cancer has returned as secondaries, even if she is *doing really well*, whatever that's supposed to mean. I don't have much choice, though, as we're going to be sitting together in the same room for the couple of hours it takes for the infusion to release itself into our bodies.

I expected someone with secondaries to be hairless, gaunt and sick-looking. When I walk into the room, I'm surprised, and relieved, to see a chubby woman in her fifties with black hair and rosy cheeks.

'This illness is such a bloody inconvenience,' she tells me once the doctor's left the room. 'It takes up so much time. Trips to the hospital for radio, the counselling, the healing, these infusions and always thinking about my diet. I never have enough time to research the book I'm supposed to be writing, let alone do the gardening or see my friends.'

'What's healing?'

'Oh, it's brilliant. This really nice guy called Chris comes over every couple of weeks. He just sits there and holds my hand and sends healing into me. He says he can see inside your body.'

She catches my expression. 'I know it sounds mad. But my scans have been improving ever since I started seeing him. Usually with secondaries it's the other way round, of course.'

I'm sceptical, but intrigued.

'Do you tell people you've got cancer?' I ask her, later.

'First time round I told almost no one. But now I just think, sod it. I was even at an opening at the Tate the other day and Nick Serota, whom I vaguely know, said "How are you?" in that way you just expect someone to answer with a "Fine, thanks." So, I said "I've got cancer." He stood there with his mouth open. It was quite funny, actually.'

A week before my second session of chemotherapy, I wake up and notice several hairs lying on the pillow. I try and tell myself I'm just being paranoid, that it's normal to lose some hair every day. But over the next few days, as I become more attentive to it, I'm sure I am losing more than usual.

A couple of mornings later, I'm in the shower, rubbing shampoo into my scalp. I bring my hands back down. They hold huge clumps of hair. Water cascades down me, carrying my hair with it. Some sticks to my arms and torso. I start crying.

I leave the shower tray coated in hair, not able to bear having to pick it up and throw it away.

My mother hears me crying and comes into my room.

'I don't know what to do. I've just lost almost all of it,' I say between sobs.

'There's still quite a lot left. Let me try and save the rest.'

'Don't touch it. You'll make it all come out.'

'I'll be very careful.'

She takes my wide-toothed wooden comb and sits next to me on the bed. Slowly and methodically, she works through my hair, taking small sections at a time and very gently drawing them through the comb or her fingers.

She detangles most of it, losing just a little more along the way. Once she's finished, I have a patchy head of hair. If I arrange it the right way, I can just about conceal the bald patches and it could still pass for a normal but fairly thin head of hair. For once I'm grateful for my naturally voluminous hair that I used to curse for being so untameable.

I am bleeding a trail of hair. It deposits itself on my pillow, my clothes, my yoga mat, my plate and sometimes even gets in my mouth. The more I lose, the more it feels like my femininity's being stripped away.

I call the oncology department and ask where I can get a good wig. They suggest Trendco on Kensington Church Street. I secretly hope that if I spend lots of money on a wig, my hair will suddenly stop falling out and I won't need it.

My mother comes with me. There are two other customers in the shop. They're Notting Hill It-girl types, about my age, and are looking for something to wear to a James Bond party. One says to the other, 'I want to be Pussy Galore from *Goldfinger*.'

'Then I'm going to be Honey Ryder from *Dr No*,' her friend replies. 'So, we both need blonde wigs.'

I hear them giggling as they try on different ones. An assistant comes up to me and asks if she can help. I lower my voice. 'I need a wig as I'm on chemo and losing a lot of hair.'

'What sort of look are you after? Do you want to try and match your real hair or go for something different? Some women use it as an opportunity to experiment with a new look.'

I'm grateful she's neither gushingly sympathetic nor embarrassed. I guess she's used to people like me.

'I just want it the same. Same colour, texture, length. So no one looking at me would guess.'

'Sit down and I'll bring over some options.'

I take a seat at the back of the room, as far away as possible from the party girls. None of the wigs she comes back with are a very close match with my own hair.

'These are all straight. Don't you do them curly, or at least wavy?'

'The artificial ones are always straight. If you want it curly we could get one made up from real hair but it'd take a few weeks and they're very expensive.'

'Like how much?'

'I'd say at least seven hundred pounds.'

I glance at my mother who's shaking her head.

'That's crazy. You'll probably either end up not needing it at all and wasting a lot of money or you'll need it before it's even ready. Just get one of the ones you've tried on. I quite liked the second last one. It's a bit darker than your hair is now and more like your natural colour. You can tell everyone you've gone back to that.'

'But it's completely straight. Everyone's going to guess.'

'I'm sure they won't. Say you've started going to the hairdresser once a week for blow drys. You always wanted straight hair, anyway.'

'Not like this.'

I ask the assistant if I can put heated rollers in to curl it.

'You can't put any heat on it. Just wash it with normal shampoo and let it dry naturally.'

'Do you do refunds, in case she doesn't need to use it?' asks my mother as she's paying.

'I'm afraid not.'

When I get home, I leave the shiny black box unopened at the back of my cupboard, hoping it can stay there.

10

I receive a text from my friend Catherine the evening before I'm due to have my second session of chemotherapy.

Alexander born at 6.15 p.m. 8lb5oz & gorgeous. Know u got chemo 2moro Would love 2 c u before if u have time?

Over months I watched her belly swell, touched it occasionally and once even felt a flutter against my hand, never imagining that while her body nurtured a baby, mine was growing a tumour.

When I arrive at the hospital, Alexander's lying in his crib. He's soft and pink with tightly shut eyes and curled fists. He's only belonged to this world for the past fifteen hours and is the newest baby I've ever seen. I'm the first of Catherine's friends to meet him. I stroke his head. It's covered in a light down.

'I was so emotional when I first saw him.' Catherine looks tired but still beautiful. 'I couldn't stop crying.'

I leave the maternity ward and walk the short distance to the chemotherapy ward. Today, I notice a very sick-looking woman in the waiting room. Both her face and body are contorted and twisted as if she's been sculpted by the force of cancer. Her skin is stretched tight over her bones. She scares me. The only spare seat is next to her.

'I was so ill last time. I had no idea it would be that bad,' I tell Dr Jones.

'It doesn't hit most people so hard. Let's try and change your anti-sickness medication around.'

'I've also lost a lot of hair. Is there any chance it'll stop now and I'll get to keep the rest?'

She gently pulls at a couple of strands.

'It is coming away very easily. I'm afraid the chances are you're going to lose most of it. I could be wrong, though, so by all means keep on wearing the ice cap if you can bear it.'

The very sick-looking woman is already in the chemotherapy room when I arrive, sitting in the corner, a drip sticking out of her twig arm. I sit as far away from her as possible.

The nurses give me the ice cap. Tanya and Paola join me and we chat and read magazines as the drugs are fed into me.

At the end, Breda, the nurse, hands me a white paper bag filled with medication. 'This time I'm sure you'll have no problems.'

'How are you feeling?' asks Paola.

'Not too bad. Well, at least not yet.'

'Tea at Aveda, then?'

We sit at a pavement table and order fresh mint tea and a selection of cakes. This café's the reason I went to work for Jamie. When it opened a few years ago, I loved the raw, pared down, wood and concrete interior, as well as the food, and asked who the architect was. I wrote to him a year later when I was looking for a new job. It was good timing as he just happened to be hiring.

'Last time, I ate all this healthy stuff after and haven't been able to face brown rice since.' I take a forkful of chocolate fudge cake. 'So, I figure it's better to eat all the unhealthy stuff straight after and hopefully it'll put me off it.'

In the evening, I am sick again. I lie awake for hours, trapped in the same repetitive cycle. Tonight, it's only fourteen times, though. When my stomach's finally empty it continues to make

85

the same motions even though nothing more comes out. I swallow capful after capful of the mint-flavoured mouthwash they gave me, but I can still taste the chemicals.

I hear the traffic on the main road whirr past. It's about 2 a.m. on Friday morning and I picture black cabs carrying people home from clubs, bars, dinner parties. Eventually, the traffic softens, the birds start to sing and, as darkness yields to a pale dawn, I fall asleep.

When I slowly begin to move through the summer days again, it often feels as if I'm the only person in this city who's not just having fun. London glows. I pass cafes and restaurants, their outdoor tables full. In Regent's Park Road, the main drag of Primrose Hill village, the scent of roast lamb wafts out of the Greek restaurant, making the street feel like a holiday resort. In front of the Queen's Head, the pub on the edge of the park, the pavement's jammed with people, pint glasses in hand. The park itself has become a giant dining room, scattered with disposable barbeques in the mornings.

It's so easy to assume things are just constructed of what's visible, to forget the hidden architecture of this city. But behind its surfaces, there are other stories, too.

While many drink wine at pavement tables, there are always others; in hospitals, hospices or at home, sick or dying through these soft summer evenings. And even behind the surfaces of some of those apparently carefree faces I enviously watch, I'm sure there are also other stories. It's just that they, like me, can hide them well.

Aunt Ann invites me over for tea again. Last time I was there she told me that while she's so sad about what's happened, at least she's getting to spend more time with me. I used to see her only every couple of months. We'd usually go out for supper, often for a curry at her favourite restaurant, The Great Nepalese near Euston Station. When we were children, she'd take me and Tanya on outings for the day. Now she always wants to see us separately, 'So I can give each of you my full attention.' More recently she hasn't been too well, so instead I would bring the occasional takeaway round after work, which she insisted on serving off her pretty blue and white German china, never letting the foil cartons near the dining table.

Something's wrong with her heart and she's got problems with her circulation, which means she can't walk properly. 'It's from all those years of smoking sixty a day,' my mother once said.

When I ring the doorbell, there's no reply. I keep pressing. These days she rarely leaves the flat and when we spoke yesterday she said how much she was looking forward to seeing me. I call my mother, unwanted images of Ann collapsed inside the flat coming to me. My mother says she'll try and get hold of the girl who comes in every morning.

'I spoke to her,' she tells me a few minutes later. 'Ann was feeling really bad this morning so they called an ambulance and took her to St Mary's. Her heart's quite weak, but apparently she's stable and already bossing all the doctors and nurses around!'

I visit her the next day. I press the metal lift button to take me up to the Zachary Cope ward on the tenth floor and realise I'm no longer quite so scared of hospitals and of seeing people who are sick. These days, I can't afford to be.

Ann's sitting up in bed and they've taken off the bandages she usually has wrapped round her feet. They are swollen and covered in crusty black scabs of dried blood.

'My darling, I'm so glad you came, but look at you, you've become so thin, and have you started to lose your hair? This is so unfair.'

I look at her. I have lost weight, but she must weigh at least a stone less, and is scrawny rather than slender. And her hair's thinned so much over the years that she barely has more than I do.

She tells me how much she misses not being able to go anywhere anymore and how she longs to see all the new exhibitions, operas, plays and go out for dinner. I'm reminded of all the outings we did as children: Southwark Cathedral, Cutty Sark, the Museum of Childhood in Bethnal Green, Kew Gardens. We'd sit in her Mini eating the homemade fudge that Tanya and I would never mention to our health-conscious mother.

I know how frustrated I've been, sick and housebound for just a few days after each chemo. But at least most of the time I can still go where I want. What must it be like to be almost permanently confined to a small flat?

She falls asleep while we're chatting. I stand by the window. To my left, the sky is streaked with pink and orange. In the distance, I can just about see the planes lining up to land at Heathrow. Directly in front of me, cranes rise out of a huge crater in the ground. It's the Paddington Basin site, a new section of city being constructed. Anne will probably never see it finished.

An Indian woman hands out trays of food and the ward fills with their congealed smell. Beyond the building site, the Westway floats on concrete pillars. While Ann sleeps and the other patients eat their dinner, I watch the rush-hour traffic slowly snaking home.

I haven't had a period in over two months. Now I long for the discomfort of backache, swollen breasts and bloating.

Dr Jones told me they usually, but not always, return after treatment in someone my age.

Now, I have an inverted cycle. Every three weeks I am filled with syringes of red liquid, as my body loses its ability to release blood.

My hair continues to fall out. My scalp is now a patch-work of exposed skin with a random scrubland of hair. It's becoming increasingly hard to cover all the bare areas. I take the wig out of its box and try it on. There are still a few longer bits of hair left which stick out beneath the wig. I know I should just shave it all off but I can't quite bring myself to. Instead, I book an appointment to have it cut again.

I didn't know where to go for the haircut. This time, there's no pretending. Paola suggested her hairdresser, Philippe. 'He's very sweet. I can call him before and explain everything.'

Tanya comes with me. When we arrive, Philippe places his hand on my shoulder. 'Don't worry I'll dry cut it. That way you'll lose less. I promise to be very gentle.' The three of us are silent as he cuts. Occasionally, I catch his dark eyes in the mirror.

I speak to Paola the next day and she tells me she happened to run into him on Marylebone High Street that morning.

'Did he say anything about me?' I ask.

'He told me you were lovely and then he said, "It's so sad, she's so young." But I told him I was sure you were going to be absolutely fine.'

I try the wig on again.

'I promise you don't look like you've got fake hair,' Tanya tells me. 'I'd make you go and find another one if you did.' But it still feels awkward to be sticking something artificial on my head.

I first wear it out to meet my ex-boss, Anthony, for lunch in Clerkenwell. For the past four years, I have come to this part of London almost every weekday. Initially, to Anthony's office on Old Street, and then to Jamie's, tucked away just behind it. It's a part of town dense with architects' practices. This is the first time I've been back in over two months.

Walking from Barbican Tube, I watch people on their lunch breaks doing the same things I used to: buying fruit from the old lady with the beehive and bright red lips on Goswell Road, queuing up for cash at the HSBC on the corner and getting organic soup from my favourite place, The Quiet Revolution.

Inevitably, I see a few familiar faces - former colleagues and people I was at university with. Conscious of the wig's elastic round my scalp, I feel as if my secret's painted across my skull. But no one looks at me at all strangely.

Anthony's work partner, Sarah, comes past me, as rushed and fashionable as ever, and in one breath says, 'Great hair - wow you're looking skinny.' A couple of Januarys ago, we briefly joined the local Weightwatchers together, wanting to shed our post-Christmas pounds. We spent the next few weeks obsessing about how to get the most out of our eighteen allocated daily points and comparing who was losing more weight until we both got thrown out for being below their permitted weight.

'So, how've you been?' asks Anthony. 'I had the feeling from your last email something was up. When I asked your friend Nicole - you know she now works for me - she said I needed to ask you.'

'I was diagnosed with breast cancer a couple of months ago.'

'How awful. My mother went through that.'

'Did she recover?'

He pauses. 'Unfortunately, not. It came back in her bones a few years later.'

I try to be bright, even though comments like this always unsettle me. 'The doctors told me I've got a good prognosis.'

'Well, I just hope everything turns out OK for you.'

My parents have a party to celebrate the fortieth anniversary of my father founding his tax consultancy business. About fifty people are coming. Will any of them notice the small line of mesh exposed along my parting or a tendril of real hair escaping? I really don't feel like making small talk to my dad's friends and work colleagues.

'Can't I just stay upstairs?' I ask my mother.

'Think how upset he'll be if you do that.' He'd never say as much, but she is right.

I put on the high-heeled sandals I bought in a discount store in New York and have never worn, a short skirt, and lots of make-up. If I'm going to have to be sociable, I want to look as glamorous and well as possible. I'm also hoping to detract attention from my hair. It doesn't work.

It really suits you.

I actually prefer it this way - it frames your face so well.

Can I have the number of your hairdresser? someone even asks.

I tell them I had it done free at Harrods and can't remember the name of the person who cut it. I change the subject. 'I'm designing the new salon there.'

For the first time in my life I've become inured to telling lies. It's frightening how easily they slide out. Until now, I'd always thought of myself as very honest. But what's shocking is how little guilt I feel, because I think it's my right to keep this hidden. I've developed my own code language. When I tell people I'm away for the weekend, it means I'll be at home throwing up from chemo. When I'm 'on my way to a meeting,' I might be heading to the oncology unit.

At the end of the party, a man in his sixties comes up to me.

'You're so lovely you know,' he slurs. 'Just delightful. Married yet?'

'No.'

91

'How about dinner sometime?'

'I'm afraid my boyfriend wouldn't be too happy about that.' I walk away.

'Who's that?' I ask my mother.

'One of your father's alcoholic friends.'

My mother's definition of an alcoholic is anyone who drinks more than three glasses of wine a day.

'It's actually very sad as he lost his wife a couple of years ago,' she continues. 'Every time I've seen him since he's drunk.'

'How did she die?' It's a question I always now ask.

'Cancer. But it was a different kind. And much more advanced than yours when they found it.'

At night, when I remove the wig, I stare at myself in the mirror, traverse the strange territory of my head. The lack of hair makes my eyes seem bigger, my cheekbones more defined.

'I like seeing your face,' my dad would say when I used to occasionally tie my hair back. 'You've got good bone structure.'

It's not a look I would share with anyone else, but actually I prefer myself without the wig. I'm more like me.

11

There must be thousands of women who share my situation but I don't know any of them. My own friends all seem to be getting engaged and married this year.

I walk around London and find myself looking at others my age. Do any of them also carry this other life? I pay close attention to the ones with shaved heads or number one haircuts, especially when their faces look drained. Are they just cool or hung-over, or are their unadorned scalps symbolic of a certain rite of passage they've also been forced to go through? I long to approach them and ask. Of course, I never do.

I'm no longer at ease in a body that has stopped looking and feeling the way I expect it to. The only benefit is I am now very thin. Within three months I've lost almost a stone. It's from a combination of throwing up and not being able to eat properly for days after chemo, as well as my healthy diet. For the first time in my life I've reached my own fantasy weight, the one where all of life's problems are supposed to disappear.

I love going into shops and trying on clothes. The once snug size tens now fall away from my skin. I have to suppress a smile as I ask for an eight. In shop mirrors, I gaze at the flatness of my stomach, the jut of my hipbones and narrowness of my thighs. But I can admire only the outlines. Inside, I feel sexless, unattractive.

I almost always leave empty-handed. I'm not earning at the moment and the only money I'm getting each month is my £265.65 statutory sick pay. My parents have generously agreed to support me until I get the money through from my flat sale. While I can justify spending their money on yoga classes or organic food, it doesn't seem quite right to be using it for clothes. In any case, most of the time I only feel like wearing comfortable things like old jeans, Birkenstocks.

You look great.

Have you lost weight?

I wish I knew your secret.

I am told this repeatedly by those who don't know. How thin I would have to get before anyone actually started to be concerned? Or would they just carry on telling me I looked more and more fantastic? A friend who was once anorexic told me how more men than ever had chatted her up then. Except she didn't feel attractive inside, either.

I start having counselling. Those close to me say things like, *You're dealing with this really well* or, *I'm sure it's all going to work out fine.* I'm glad they believe in me, but sometimes I also want to be able to share my fears and losses.

I was talking to a family friend at a party last autumn. Her brother, who's about my age, was diagnosed with kidney cancer the year before.

'He's pretty good at the moment, considering,' she told me. 'And he's been seeing an amazing therapist. A Spanish guy, who's really helping him come to terms with it all.'

I call her to ask for the therapist's number, pretending I need it for a friend. When I phone up, he tells me he's not really taking on new patients right now. But as soon as I explain why I need to see him he says, 'I only work in London on Thursdays, but I'll make sure I find you a space.'

His clinic is in a semi-detached thirties house on a quiet street behind the Kilburn High Road. Waiting, paying for and booking appointments all take place in a tiny hallway, just beyond the swing of the front door. There are a couple of chairs next to an urn of hot water and a box of herbal teabags. A middle-aged bearded man sits behind a desk, listening to *Classic FM*.

Javier appears. He is also middle-aged and bearded. He has kind eyes and a reassuring handshake. We go up to an attic room furnished with a bed, a desk, a coffee table and three chairs.

In heavily accented but precise English, Javier subjects me to the rigours of his new patient questionnaire: 'Do you get many headaches?...Do you usually orgasm when you have intercourse?...Have you ever tried to commit suicide?' Then he asks for the details of my cancer, before closing the session, almost exactly fifty minutes later.

'Would you like to see me every week?' he offers.

I'd quite like to run away and never come back. Scraping below the surface is going to be awkward and painful. But even though I didn't enjoy his interrogations, I'm impressed by their thoroughness and he seems compassionate and thoughtful.

'Yes.'

'Good. Tell Peter at reception I want you to have an appointment every Thursday.'

'I'm afraid there are no appointments with Javier for at least the next couple of months. He's completely booked up.' Peter's tone is intractable.

'But he told me...'

'It doesn't matter what he told you. I make the appointments.'

Self-important little tosser. Suddenly, I badly want counselling.

Javier calls the next day.

'I've told Peter you're one of my top priority patients and he's to give you an appointment every week.'

'I think we need to look at whether there are things in your emotional life which could have contributed to the cancer,' says Javier, the following week. 'Can you tell me a bit more about the relationship with that man, Markus, in Berlin, the one you mentioned briefly last week?'

Hearing his name reminds me of things I thought I'd forgotten. His hands and smile, the icy winter we spent together in a flat in East Berlin where the coal stove was broken, but even that didn't seem to really matter.

I start telling Javier how I met him there in the mid-nineties. It was my first day at work, a new job in a new city. He opened the office door and offered to make me a coffee. A fellow architect, tall, curly-haired, smiley. I liked him immediately.

I knew no one in Berlin. I'd come because England was deep in recession and there was no work for architects. In Berlin, the new capital of a recently reunified Germany, I was offered eight jobs within three days.

On my first Friday evening, he invited me out with his friends after work. Beers at the high-ceilinged Café Einstein, once the drawing room of Henny Porten, Germany's first ever movie star, Markus told me. Later, at a club somewhere near the Wall, we danced to 'It's Raining Men'. At 5 a.m., we finished with breakfast at the *Schwarzes* Café, ham, cheese and bread soaking up the alcohol.

I returned to my rented room in *Schonenberg* and lay in bed, too excited to sleep. Opposite my window, the church bells pealed every quarter hour. I could think only of him.

A week later, we met under the *Alexanderplatz* Tower. Breakfast in *Prenzlauer Berg* became a daylong meander through the quiet Sunday streets of East Berlin. He showed me his favourite places. One, a turn of the century building with seven interconnected tiled courtyards. In the seventh, we could hear nothing but birdsong.

After a vodka party at his flat in East Berlin two long weeks later, I finally realised he felt the same as I did. We had our first kiss to a Tom Waits song, 'I Hope That I Don't Fall In Love With You.' After that night, we were constantly together.

'Are you afraid to fall in love?' he asked a few weeks later.

'This feels too good to be scared of.'

Six months in, he gave me a ring for Christmas, a simple silver band with a continuous line carved round the centre. 'I bought it for you because the line in the middle suggests something which can just go on and on.'

We broke up at the end of the following year. A few months earlier I'd moved back to England to finish my studies. We promised we'd make it work.

'It's only two years,' he said. But with both of us suddenly in different places, it stopped working. In Berlin we spent almost all our time together. But living separate lives, we somehow lost the thread. He was five years older, very passionate about architecture and determined to make it. He got a new job just before I left and was always working on some competition deadline or another. When I was in Berlin it didn't bother me too much as I'd still see him every night, even if sometimes he didn't get home until the early hours. Once I moved back, and he cancelled a couple of weekends we were meant to be seeing each other, because of work, I got annoyed. He thought I was unsupportive and didn't understand that he was in a job where he had to do this, at an important stage in his career.

I'd sometimes tell my friends I was going to leave him as I was tired of coming second after architecture. I never really meant it. And naively, I thought he adored me so much he'd never finish with me. But he did.

It was in a café off Piccadilly with green plastic bucket seats and steamed-up windows. I was devastated. However fed up I was, I really loved him. I tried to convince him to give it another chance. But the magic had gone.

I took him back to Heathrow and cried all the way home on the Tube. Afterwards, I blamed myself with if onlys, my mind deconstructing every letter, conversation and meeting we had since I left Berlin: if only I'd done this or that differently, perhaps we'd still be together?

Even now, when I look back to my time in that strange broken city, where I stayed out too late and drank too much beer and coffee, it's with nostalgia and regret, and a longing to return to the intensity of falling in love, both with him and with Berlin.

For a long time, I looked for him in everyone I met. Even though it happened some years ago, there've been only occasional encounters since - a few weeks here, a couple of months there. I'd always say I was unlucky in love, that I never met the right person, or when I did they already had a girlfriend. My mother has a different opinion.

'You're just too fussy. Always looking for what doesn't exist. They don't have to be perfect, you know.'

The problem was, in so many ways Markus was. We had great chemistry, could talk endlessly about architecture, art, literature, and shared a sense of humour. He was kind, decent and gentle and had really loved me. Ironically, one of the things that drew me to him in the first place was that he was such a talented and passionate architect.

Perhaps I've lost the ability to tumble headfirst like I did then?

But I don't understand what this has to do with cancer.

'I think you've carried a burden inside you for a long time. Blaming yourself because this relationship didn't work out,' suggests Javier.

'And you really think that could have contributed to my illness?'

'I do.'

Can we measure what imprint the events which happen to us have on our lives? Is sorrow really able to leak into our bodies?

'But loads of people go through painful break-ups. I'm not exactly unusual. I'm sure most of them don't end up with cancer. It's not even as if anything really awful happened. He didn't die or leave me for someone else. We just fell in love, broke up and I really missed him and wished we hadn't.'

'It's not so much what happens, but rather how we deal with it. In your case, I think you internalised it all and closed yourself off. Of course I'm not saying that's the only reason you got cancer. You've also just been really unlucky. But my feeling is it's part of the story. Our emotions can have a profound effect on our bodies.'

His words surprise me. It has never crossed my mind that cancer could be triggered by an emotional upset. Of course, I feel emotions in my body - the clench of my stomach when I'm afraid, or the heat in my chest when I'm angry. I even remember completely losing my voice right after Markus and I broke up. But these are immediate sensations, their cause easy to identify. The jump between something which happened years ago and this tumour seems far more tenuous. Yet I'm prepared to consider it.

Included in my chemo package were a couple of free massages at the oncology unit. A young blonde woman in a white uniform patted me as if I was a delicate object. I asked if she could make it a bit stronger.

'I'm afraid not. We've been advised to keep it very light for people having treatment.'

Usually, I feel transformed after a massage. Sometimes energised, sometimes soporific. That time, nothing.

I dig out an article I cut out of *The Evening Standard* last year about good masseurs. I keep a folder of newspaper and magazine cuttings about where to go for the best haircut, facial, pedicure and so on, even though I almost never use them. The article recommends a woman called Michelle in Maida Vale.

She works out of a pale blue two-storey terraced house in a quiet street called Violet Hill. The treatment room overlooks a church and is lit with tea lights and smells of orange oil.

Michelle is voluptuous, with dark hair, eyes and skin and large strong looking hands - *half Indian, half Irish*, the article said.

'So, tell me, what's going on in your life?'

I remember how she was quoted in the article.

I see busy people who, on the surface are very well put-together; but when I touch them I can feel how vulnerable they are.

'I was diagnosed with breast cancer recently. I'm having chemotherapy at the moment.'

'When I shook your hand, I wondered what had happened. You felt like cotton wool.'

We talk for a few minutes before she starts the massage.

'I'm wearing a wig. Can I keep it on?'

'I'd rather you didn't as I'd like to work on your head. Please don't feel uncomfortable. I've seen all this before.'

She pours oil into her hands, telling me that today she's using chamomile, jasmine and neroli. With firm strokes she spreads it across my back. I start to soften. Having become a receptacle for needles and strange fluids, it's a relief to be touched properly again. I'd come to associate touch with fear: a doctor's fingers palpating my breast as I lie there, tense, awaiting his response; my own hands, anxiously searching across my skin; the repeated sharp stab of the canula in my arm as it attempts to connect to a vein.

Lying here, I'm reminded of another massage I once had. It was a couple of weeks after Markus and I broke up and I thought it might help to cheer me up. I cried all the way through, though. It was the first time since we split that anyone had really touched me, and the sensation of this gentle Chinese man's hands sliding across my skin made me feel even lonelier as it brought back all the memories of Markus's touch.

Michelle's hands delve into me, waking up skin, muscles, organs. When I turn onto my back she places warm, oil-rich hands on my head, on the almost naked skin of my scalp, holding them there for what seems like several minutes. Then she massages my heart area and stomach, those sensitive places where the skin never seems thick enough.

When it's over, she leaves the room and I lie there, eyes closed, my body heavy and calm, wanting to just stay in this protective space.

She hugs me when I leave and says, 'I've got a sense that you've become a bit out of touch with yourself. You seem really disciplined but I think you need to get more in tune with your emotions and what you're really feeling.'

I like Michelle a lot, but I don't like her saying this to me. It makes me feel as if my surface has been a bit of a charade, its polished exterior hiding things that are not so smooth.

Before getting ill, it seemed like my life, apart from the absence of a boyfriend, made sense. Now, it's been thrown into disarray. I'm no longer the healthy, independent person with hair, a good job and a great social life. Having had so much of what I identified with taken away makes me no longer sure of exactly who I am, even though to people unaware of what's happened, I still seem the same.

And now I'm meeting people like Javier and Michelle who are suggesting I look inside myself and pay some attention to the places that aren't so resolved.

'Don't you think all this focusing on what's not working is just going to make me lose what's left of my confidence and identity?' I ask Javier.

'I think in the end it'll actually make you more confident. It's important to become familiar with your vulnerabilities. We all have them. They're as much a part of us as the bits that work well. But so often we pretend they're not there and get very caught up in trying to put across a good image.' He tells me that true confidence comes from accepting yourself completely.

Of course, I could choose to ignore him and Michelle and say they're talking a load of bullshit. Part of me wants to do just that. Hearing this stuff, it's easy to feel as if you're the only person in the world who's not sorted, especially as you watch everyone else rush round their busy, successful lives. What I can't escape from is how much my life has changed these past few months, and there's no use pretending it hasn't.

Another part of me wants to listen to them, to trust in the wisdom and compassion they seem to have, and is curious about the possibility of transformation. This illness has already taken me to places far beyond my comfort zone.

12

There's a small group of us who gather in a top-floor room on New Cavendish Street every Tuesday morning for vitamin infusions. It's the first chance I've had to speak to others with cancer. We're a disparate group, linked only by our illness.

At seventy-one, Len's the oldest and loves his status as the only man in the group, using it to flirt shamelessly with the rest of us. He has pancreatic cancer and his local hospital told him he had three months left and there was no point having any surgery or treatment. Hearing this saddened me. I have a soft spot for Len and his cheeky humour. He has four children, lots of grandchildren and adores his family. And he's the same age as my dad. He's already survived eight months and he says he's feeling good. 'I've even got myself a new bird - she helps keep me smiling.' She turns up with him one day, a feisty-looking Spaniard, in her early fifties, with long black ringlets.

I'm the youngest. Emma's a few years older. She's married with two children and has ovarian cancer. There's Patricia, the art historian with secondaries, and then there's Harriet, who also has breast cancer. We share a surgeon and a similar prognosis, except she's been spared chemo as she's postmenopausal. She makes me laugh when she tells me how she's planning to go to her next check up with our surgeon wearing a black basque and stockings. Harriet weighs about fifteen stone.

A beautiful, tanned blonde woman in her forties turns up occasionally. She looks far too healthy to have cancer. Perhaps she's here for a bit of general detoxing? But she tells us her breast cancer has come back in her liver. 'I did really well those first five years.' I shiver when I hear that.

We all chat during the couple of hours it takes for the infusions to drip into us. Cancer dominates our conversations. Usually, it's a relief to be among people who are comfortable discussing it. Sometimes, though, when someone has bad results to share, I wish I didn't have to know. And when from one week to the next someone doesn't show and we don't know why, I hope it's not because they're suddenly worse.

One thing we don't talk about is whether we're afraid. Instead, we tell each one another about our treatments, alternative and conventional, and compare notes on what we've been told we can and can't eat. We debate whether honey is allowed or if it still counts as sugar, and exchange tips on where to find dairy and sugar-free organic biscuits.

Harriet's still smoking forty a day. She's trying her best with the diet but her interpretation of it seems rather broad.

'I mean, darling,' she says to me, 'When you say you're not drinking or eating sugar, you do mean only at home? After all, you can't go to The Ivy and not have their sticky toffee pud and a nice glass of dessert wine. And it's so hard to resist cheese and biscuits after supper.'

Occasionally someone who hasn't got cancer joins us for an infusion as they're also supposed to be good for ME, or just giving you an extra boost of energy. What's it like for them to be among us and our conversations? I know that not so long ago I'd have been quite freaked out to be thrown into a room with a group of cancer patients.

It is now the end of July. I haven't been at work for almost three months. Would the novelty wear off after a while? But I don't miss being in an office - the rush-hour Tube journeys, long hours, constant deadlines and sudden problems on site, always needing to be dealt with that minute.

When I was working, I'd sometimes long for space to open up around me, rather than everything always feeling compressed. The other day, I looked back through my notebook, in which I write my to-do lists as well as musings on what I want from my life. Only in March, I wrote, *I wish I had more time. Time to look after myself, to be still, to do things like meditation.* Not that I'd have chosen to acquire it this way.

Last summer, sitting at my desk in Jamie's elegant concrete and black steel office, sometimes I'd look out of the window, at the patch of blue sky and leafy branches visible above the buildings, and wish I could just be lying in the park with a book.

This summer, I can. The only thing I have to do is go to chemotherapy every three weeks. Accompanying the awfulness of it all is a strange sense of luxury and release at having been able to step away from the structure of my old life, and into this slow-paced one.

I get up when I want, take long baths laced with essential oils, meditate, read the papers over a leisurely breakfast. Typically, I spend my days going to yoga, reading in the garden, sometimes meeting friends for lunch.

Someone suggested I do only restorative yoga - which you do lying down and relaxing over various props such as bolsters and blankets - while going through treatment. But I find I need the more active classes, as they remind me of my strength, of my aliveness. That not all is lost.

I also spend a lot of time in Primrose Hill and Regent's Park, walking, or just lying on the grass in the sun or under a tree. These spaces feel as if they've been severed from the busy rhythm of the surrounding city. Mothers amble with prams and toddlers, couples pause to watch the birds by the lake in Regent's Park. A tramp sits on a bench, his closed eyes raised to the sun, a crumpled beer can by his side. And I find myself paying attention to and feeling a connection to things I never used even to notice, as if my senses have been recalibrated: the patterns a flock of birds create against the sky; the beds of tulips in Regent's Park so scarlet they look as if they've been injected with artificial colour; the shifting shapes of the clouds. It's ironic how we're often only able really to appreciate things when they become threatened.

Of course, there's also a dark underbelly to these days. At times this world I now inhabit feels like a sanctuary, at others a cage. Some days I'm thinking it's great to have a summer off, others I'm angry and frightened. Angry that cancer's stopped my life in its tracks and made it so out of synch with everyone else's. Angry that I'll probably always have to live under the shadow of this illness and that I'll never be able to return to the innocence of simply trusting my body. And while at times I manage to convince myself that it's all going to be fine in the end, at others I am doubtful: not everything does come right. Awful things do happen. Why do you think you'll be immune? Cancer's not been given the death sentence label for nothing.

The fear often hits me hardest in the early hours. Since starting chemotherapy, I'm not sleeping properly. Almost every night I'm wide awake around three, sweating, my heart pounding. However many times I change position or just try and breathe slowly and calmly, I can't get back to sleep. It's at these times, along the shoreline between darkness and dawn, that my mind often whispers to me: there is so much you will never get to taste. This has really fucked everything up.

An upside of the fear that I could die is that it does shift my perspective. I realise I've no idea how much time I have left - of course none of us do, but this was never something I thought much about before - so it makes me want to live the rest of my life, however long or short, in a way which makes me truly happy.

It's not that I was unhappy before. But there were things I'd sometimes wish could be different. I wanted more freedom, and ideally to be my own boss. I'd also periodically question whether I wanted to carry on being an architect. I've always longed for a career where I can't imagine doing anything else, rather than one I just quite like. I studied architecture because I loved drawing and painting and was interested in buildings. I enjoy designing, but find myself spending much more of my time doing things like dealing with the contractual side, the builders, construction details, the endless meeting minutes. And the hours are long, the job inherently stressful.

Even though I used to think about doing something else - such as setting up an organic food business or a spa, writing about architecture and urbanism, or at least working for myself as an architect - these were just daydreams. I'd also remind myself that I was lucky to have a job I at least quite liked, which is more than a lot of people have.

Now, anything seems possible. I've added yoga teacher and masseur to the list of possible careers, as well as lots of travel plans - Patagonia, Chile, Japan, Australia, New Zealand. I tell myself I'm going to be sure to use this illness as a catalyst for making some changes.

I don't go out late much these days and spend most of my time with my family and the handful of friends who know the truth.

One day I get an email from Michael inviting everyone to a party he's having at a bar in South Kensington. Ioana and I met him through a friend last year. He's half Swiss and half American, and one of these people who seem to know absolutely everyone. We used to sometimes go along to the informal get-togethers he'd hold at The Chepstow pub in Notting Hill most Thursday evenings. 'Michael's salon,' we'd joke.

Before I got ill, he was vaguely talking about getting me to work with him on a spa and retreat centre he was planning in Italy.

'I've found an old castle in the hills north of Genoa. I want to make it somewhere busy people can escape to and get back in touch with themselves and nature. Sounds as if you could be the perfect person to design it.' I haven't seen him in months, though.

Ioana calls to ask if I'm going to the party.

'I'm not particularly in a party mood. But I'll probably try and go for a bit.' I want him to still keep me in mind for his spa.

I arrange to meet Ioana outside the bar at nine-thirty. It's strange to be starting my evening at the time I'm often already in bed. I've also not been out to a big party since this all started. I put on jeans, which now need a belt, and the New York sandals.

I drive through Hyde Park to South Kensington. The half-lit city rises beyond the darkening canopies of trees. The Serpentine gleams pale grey. This is my favourite time, where the city seems to pause briefly as it hovers between night and day.

The bar's already crowded. Bollywood music plays and the ceilings are draped with silk fabric, the walls painted bright pink. Michael glides over to kiss us hello, his white shirt accentuating his tan from a recent trip to Sri Lanka.

'Hey, I'm keen to get you over to Italy to have a look at the site in the next few weeks,' he says to me. 'Email me your schedule and I'll organise flights.' A blonde guy joins us. 'Joachim, meet Annabel and Ioana, very good friends of mine. I must go and do some more introductions. We'll catch up properly later.'

'What do you do?' I ask Joachim.

'I'm a clinical psychiatrist.'

'And where do you work?'

'At the Maudsley in south London.'

These days I find myself more interested in the medical world so I ask lots of questions.

'It's really interesting, though tough at times. I have a lot of patients with schizophrenia.' He smiles at me and says jokingly, 'You look far too well to have any problems yourself, of course.'

A tall, very handsome man joins us. 'This is my friend Andreas,' says Joachim.

'So, what do you do?' Andreas asks me.

'I'm an architect.'

'Thank God, another creative person. It's full of bankers here. I'm a designer, too.'

We chat for a while, until Kwong, in his banker's suit, comes over. 'Where've you been, stranger? I haven't seen you in, like, months.' The last time I saw him was when we had falafel on Edgware Road, the night I found the lump. It's good to catch up again but I'm wishing he hadn't broken up my conversation with Andreas.

Andreas comes back later, though. 'I'm leaving now, but it was really nice to meet you. Let me get your details so we can catch up again.'

It's almost one when Ioana and I leave. 'What a result, that guy's seriously gorgeous. I'm so happy for you,' she says.

I drive home, down Knightsbridge, passing Harrods, its skin strung with the necklaces of a thousand lights.

13

There's already an email in my inbox the next morning.

It was great to meet you last night. How about a drink next week?

I slightly panic. Do hairless people on chemo actually go out on dates?

I call Paola.

'Don't be silly. You're still gorgeous, still the same person. Anyway, it's only a drink. You're not marrying him or anything.'

'It was a lovely boost to get his message. But I'm not sure I really want a boyfriend right now. I feel much too unattractive and caught in this whole sickness world. I think I should just focus on getting better.'

'When I met Costas the last thing I wanted was a relationship. I was totally into my work. And look what happened there. Speaking of which, is August thirty-first OK for my hen night or does it clash with chemo? I just want a quiet dinner with you, Catherine, Mel and Ayala.'

I calculate the dates in my head. 'It's a week after the fourth one so I'll be fine by then.'

I email Andreas back suggesting we meet the following Thursday. My third session of chemotherapy is tomorrow, so I should be better by then.

I'm sitting in Dr Jones's office the next day when a nurse comes in and hands her a sheet of paper. She looks at it and frowns.

'I'm afraid you can't actually have chemo today. The blood test shows your white cell count's way too low. Come back in a week. By then it should have recovered.'

'Why's it so low?'

'Chemo attacks healthy cells as well as unhealthy ones. Which means your white cell count, basically an indicator of how well your immune system's functioning, can be affected. It's quite common.'

'But I'm supposed to be going to Italy with my family. We specially booked it so it wouldn't coincide with chemo. Can't I just have it anyway?'

'Unfortunately not. You'll have to cancel the holiday. There'll be others. What's most important is that you get better.'

How can I be sure there will be others?

When I was first diagnosed, images of some of the things I might never get to experience again passed through my mind. One was of the Dolomite mountains in the far north of Italy, crowned by spires, towers and reefs of rock that glow pink in certain lights, and where I'd walk through pine and larch forests or meadows sprinkled with wildflowers, the air crisp yet warm.

I've been there several times on family holidays over the years. Last time, a hiking guide told me how they rose out of an ancient sea called the Thetis which originated over two hundred and fifty million years ago. It always amazes me how places can exist for that long. Thinking about geological time makes the span of a human life seem tiny.

When he found out I was an architect he said, 'Did you know that Le Corbusier described the Dolomites as the most beautiful piece of architecture in the world?' I loved them even more after that.

I don't want to have to go home and tell my mother why I haven't had chemo and why I can't come on holiday. I head to Marylebone High Street and look round the shops, trying on perfume and body lotions in Space NK. I spend ages in Daunt Books, browsing through the piles stacked up on the wooden tables. I buy a chick lit novel called *Thirtynothing*, which I'll save for post-chemo days and, to balance it, a serious one Aunt Ann recommended called *Austerlitz*, about a Second World War refugee. I walk home through Regent's Park, pausing on the grass by the boating lake to lie in the sun.

When I arrive home, my mother says, 'That was quick. I thought we agreed you'd call before you finished so I could pick you up. I hope you took a taxi and didn't walk.'

'I didn't have it.'

'What?'

I tell her in the briefest most optimistic outline about the white blood cells.

'I don't like the sound of this. How can you be sure this isn't an indication of more cancer? I want you to get to the bottom of it.'

'You're being ridiculous. I've told you it happens to loads of people. There's no need to overreact as usual.'

'I'm sure it has something to do with that crazy diet of yours. You're eating virtually no protein, existing on fruit and vegetables and you've lost so much weight. No wonder your immune system's down.'

My voice rises. 'It's nothing to do with it. How dare you criticise my diet. You've been waiting for a chance to do that. You should be proud I've taken such a proactive approach. My diet's much better than yours or anyone else's I know. Look in any nutrition book and it'll tell you it's what everyone, cancer or no cancer, should be doing.'

'In any case, how can I even be sure you've been telling me the truth about what all these doctors say to you? You refuse to let me come with you to any appointments. You've left me completely out of the picture.'

Rational speech has evaporated. The louder my voice becomes the stronger hers bounces back. I am furious at her for reacting in this way. How dare she stress me out like this.

'Why do you think I won't let you come? Because you'd interfere and ask all sorts of ridiculous questions. I want to do things my way.'

'That's your bloody problem, always having to do it your way. Only thinking of yourself. Have you ever stopped to think about how it feels for me, watching my daughter go through this?'

In frustration, I grab an empty saucepan from the kitchen worktop and throw it across the floor. It bounces on the tiles, changes direction and accidentally hits her, splitting the skin just above the ankle. Blood leaks out.

I stop shouting and start crying.

'I can't believe I did that. I swear I didn't mean it to hit you. You know how much I love you. I'd never want to hurt you.'

I look at her, trying to stem the flow of blood with a piece of kitchen roll. I see how she's no longer made of strength and anger, but vulnerable, old. I try to put my arms round her but she pushes me away. 'Please, just leave me alone for today.'

I go upstairs and lie down on my bed, still crying.

I hate you so much, I tell the cancer.

I spend the rest of the day remorseful and angry for having lost my temper. She's right. I don't often think about how it feels for her. I took her smiling face and her repeated, *Don't worry, darling, it's all going to be all rights*, as proof she was coping well. I have been focused on myself. But perhaps I've had to be. And perhaps it's too painful to really think about what it must be like for her, my father, my sister.

None of us voices our true feelings. We all hide our fear, and they express their love and concern through action, not language. My mother drives me around, buys me the organic food I request, sits with me when I'm sick. My father hugs me a lot. My sister wants to be with me all the time.

Over the next couple of days, the atmosphere in the house is gloomy and heavy, mirroring the wet, grey August weather. I've apologised again and again and she's said in a dull voice, 'Let's just move on from this,' but I can tell she's still angry and hurt. Behind closed doors I catch fragments of murmured telephone conversations with Tanya - '...being really difficult...I know she's having a hard time but it's hard for me, too.'

She's not saying much to me but she does offer to cancel the trip to Italy so she's here after I've had chemo. I tell her to go. 'It'll be good for you and Dad to get away. Anyway, Tanya's insisting on staying behind, so there's no point you all being here.'

Secretly, I'm quite glad she's going to be away for a week.

For weeks I've been thinking about calling the healer Patricia mentioned. Despite what she told me about her scans improving, healing still sounded flaky and insubstantial, something to be used only by the desperately sick or desperately rich. The first time I call, I put the phone down, put off by the happy clappy voice on his voicemail. I picture someone in an orange robe with a nose ring and a shaved head.

'He's not like that at all,' Patricia reassures me. 'Just a nice, normal guy.'

I call back and we arrange to meet two days before I'm due to go back for chemo. I'm surprised to open the door to a tall, slim guy in his forties with big green eyes, wearing Levis, a navy sweatshirt and Timberlands. He's even rather good looking.

We sit down on the sofa and he takes my left hand in his right. His hand is large, warm and reassuring. It shouldn't feel this comfortable to have a man I've only just met holding my hand like this. Then, to my surprise, I start crying.

'I've no idea why I'm crying.' I'm embarrassed. 'I wasn't even feeling sad before you came.'

'Don't worry, it happens all the time. Anyway, it's good to have a cry. You've been through a lot.'

'How does healing work?'

'I'm like a conduit which transfers healing energy from the universe into you.'

'Do I need to believe in it for it to work?'

'No. All you need to do is sit here and hold my hand.'

After a while he says, 'You've got a really wicked sense of humour, haven't you? It feels as if you've pushed that side of you away though, and become a bit rigid and obsessed with doing the right thing rather than just being yourself. I can imagine you wanting to send really saucy texts to your boyfriend.'

'I don't have a boyfriend.'

'And I don't have a girlfriend. You know, it's not the end of the world being single.'

Briefly, I conjure up images of dating the healer. Then I remember Andreas.

'I've got a date tomorrow night with this gorgeous guy. Can the healing help make sure it goes really well?'

'Can't promise, but I'll try. It tends to go to where you need it most, and at the moment that's probably not top priority. You'll be feeling pretty shattered after this so I hope you'll have enough energy left for your date.'

I tell him about my white blood cell count, my lost hair and period and how sick the chemo's made me.

'Don't worry, your cell counts will be up again tomorrow and you won't be as sick next time. Your period should be back within a week and your hair's also going to start growing again soon. And most importantly, you won't have any more problems with cancer again'

'How can you be so sure?'

'I just am.'

Please let him be right, I pray. Especially about no more cancer.

It's the first night I sleep through until morning. When I open my eyes it's already nine-thirty. I close them again and sleep until after eleven.

There's no way I'm going to be able to stay up late tonight so I call Andreas to cancel our date.

'I'm really sorry, but I've been sprung a last-minute work deadline,' I tell his voicemail. 'Could we rearrange for next week?' Lying is now so effortless and guilt free.

My parents leave for Italy the following morning.

'I'll miss you,' I hug my mother especially tightly. Things between us are now almost back to normal. They head off to Heathrow and I return to the chemo unit.

'We're not sure you'll be able to have it today,' says the nurse. 'The blood test showed your white cell count's gone sky high. It means you're probably fighting an infection.'

'I feel absolutely fine.'

'We'll need to do a urine test to check.'

The test comes back negative.

'It's really strange having a cell count that high without an infection. I guess we'll have to let you have chemo, though.'

My phone starts ringing while the nurse is injecting the bright red Ebiprubicin. Andreas's name flashes up on the screen. I don't take it.

At the end, the nurse gives me my anti sickness medication and another white paper bag. 'Put this one in the fridge as soon as you get home. It's your *G-CSF* injections. You need to inject yourself with them for the next five days. They should stop your bloods plummeting again.'

Tanya's waiting at my parents' house when I get back. 'I'm even wearing my white Birkenstocks so I can be a proper nurse for you,' she jokes.

This is the year Birkenstocks have gone from being shoes worn only by nurses or German hippies, and become objects of desire. White is the in colour this summer and they look great on Tanya, with her blonde curls and blue eyes. I've been wearing my chocolate brown ones almost every day.

I get into bed and wait. I can hear Tanya moving around in the next room, a piano concerto, possibly Beethoven, sounding faintly through the wall. My sister trained as a violinist at The Royal Academy of Music and now teaches violin to children. This is the first time in years we've stayed in the house together.

The nausea slowly starts to rise and I brace myself. But nothing happens. I look at the clock. It's already past nine. I stay awake until after ten, and then, exhausted, slide into sleep. To my amazement, I wake up at seven having not been sick once.

I always feel a bit low the days following chemo, but this time it's worse than usual. I'm surprised, as it's the only time I haven't actually been sick. It's August but London is still sunk under a heavy sky, which refuses to open. A lot of my friends are away on holiday. I'm trapped in the middle of this. Three down, three to go.

I inject myself every day.

'Put it into a fatty area like your stomach, hips or buttocks,' the nurse told me, 'Not that there's much fat left on you.' When I do it, I never manage to insert the syringe deep enough and the clear liquid gets trapped and forms little bubbles under my skin.

I wake up one night and find blood staining my sheets. At first, I worry something's wrong. Then I realise what it is. When I go back to sleep I dream about red fluids fusing together inside me. One, which smells of chemicals, is being poured in, while another, which smells like rusty iron is being poured out.

Having been suppressed for almost three months, my period is heavier than ever, like a river that's burst its banks. For once, I am grateful to be able to feel its discomfort.

14

Andreas and I have arranged to meet at The Engineer, a pub in Primrose Hill.

I walk into the beer garden, wig on my head and my body still redolent with last week's chemotherapy. I feel like a fraud.

My eyes search the garden for the face I hope I'll still be able to recognise. I spot him before he notices me. He's on his mobile phone, glass of Pimms in his hand. Often, reality fails to match up to the image we create in our minds, especially when the only time you've ever seen someone is submerged in a basement bar. Yet in the evening light, Andreas appears even more attractive than I remembered. The blue eyes, light brown curly hair, defined face and tall, slim build are a perfect match to the unwritten specification I hold in my mind.

'It's really good to see you again.' He kisses my cheeks. 'What can I get you?'

I've given this question some thought. Would it appear too uptight to go out on a date and not drink alcohol? Is my attractiveness influenced by my choice of drink? I ask for an apple juice.

I'm nervous as I wait for him to return with my drink. What if he notices the mesh of the wig exposed where I've formed a parting, or sees the scored line of my scar escaping beyond my vest top? Things I see as if through a magnifying glass.

Conversation is easy. We have plenty of common ground; architecture, mutual friends, travel. Over the next couple of hours, we make the first few surface incisions into the process of getting to know one another. I learn that he lives in Notting Hill and loves windsurfing and skiing. He originally studied economics before changing to design. His parents live in a village in Germany near the French border, his brother in Berlin.

Even today, just hearing the word Berlin moves something inside me. I don't think it's possible to fall in love with someone and not fall in love with the place in which it happened. Andreas goes to Berlin quite often. I picture us there together, having Sunday breakfast in *Prenzlauer Berg*, drinking in *Kreuzberg*, sunbathing at the *Wannsee* lake.

The threads of his story reach out and pull me towards him. I know so little about him but it doesn't stop me.

We both really want to visit Stockholm.

'We should go there together sometime,' he suggests.

He must like me to say that.

We stay at the pub until closing time. He kisses me on the cheeks again and says 'That was nice - let's do it again soon.'

I go home, exhilarated. *Had a fab evening x*, I text my sister and she calls five seconds later wanting to know all about it. A few hours ago, I didn't even want a boyfriend. Now, I decide that a relationship could help me to heal. I lie in bed and try to sleep but my head is filled with images of him, of us.

What's the soonest he might call? It's Thursday today so it may not be until early next week. Though if he's really keen he could call at the weekend. Perhaps he's my gift in return for everything I've been through? It would almost make it worth it.

He doesn't call at the weekend.

Monday. Nothing.

Tuesday. Nothing.

Wednesday. Nothing.

Each time I hear my mobile, I immediately think, could it be him? There are those few seconds of anticipation until I see the screen and realise it's not. My sister and my friends call all the time. Instead of being pleased to hear from them, as I usually am, I'm disappointed they are not him.

Perhaps he's lost my number? Unlikely, as it's surely stored in his phone. Emailed instead? Nothing there. Maybe he's busy or away? Maybe he'll call tomorrow, the day after, next week?

I tell myself to give up. When they like you, they call. Simple, really. But I can't quite let go of hoping.

On the Thursday, I visit Aunt Ann. She's now left St Mary's and been temporarily put in a nursing home in Highgate. We sit together on the covered balcony outside her room while the summer rain falls over the garden blooming with irises, canna lilies, delphiniums. The air smells of earth. There's a continuous wail of 'BaBaBaBaBa' from the next-door room.

'It never stops, even at night,' Ann tells me. 'She's ninety-seven and the nurse told me she's been here eight years. I hope I never end up like that. Better to go sooner.'

As if possessed by a nervous tick, I glance repeatedly at my phone, switched on silent, lying on the table between us.

'I don't understand why everyone has these things now. Why on earth does one need to be available all the time?'

I was one of the last people I knew to get a mobile and used to think that, too. Now, I'd be completely lost without it.

I try and maintain a smile for Ann, who has expressed so much delight at my visit. But in keeping with the drum of the rain, the cries from the next-door room and the silence from my phone, I am melancholic.

The following week, I have my fourth session of chemotherapy. It's a grey Friday afternoon in late August. Back at home, I run a hot bath and pour in an aromatherapy oil labelled *Soothing*, hoping it will obliterate the memory of the chemicals.

I'm not sure what to do with myself. Reading is too much effort and I don't dare eat. If I shut my eyes and try to sleep, I feel dizzy. I sit down on the sofa and turn on the TV. The screen shows an image of a pair of child-sized coffins covered with flowers being carried by pallbearers. I'd forgotten that today is the funeral of Jessica Chapman and Holly Wells, the two ten-year-old girls recently murdered in Soham. It's being broadcast live from Ely Cathedral.

There are times when life sparkles so much that the light almost hurts my eyes. But without warning, the world can turn on itself, showing its dark face. Illness may have stripped me of some of my own innocence and trust in life, but in comparison to this, my own suffering feels negligible.

The sickness begins a few hours later. The scents of geranium and camomile from my bath linger on my skin and wed themselves to the taste and smell of the drugs. Perhaps I could have avoided being sick if I'd had healing this week?

My bedside table is piled with boxes of tablets with ugly-sounding names like *Ondansteron* and *Dextromythane*. They are supposed to make me feel better. Long lists of their potential side effects are printed in tiny script on the leaflets tucked away inside their boxes. I'm not used to all this medication. It's also easy to be convinced that the sickness is a symptom of the disease rather than of its cure.

Caught in chemo's web, I fantasise about escaping. I dream of hearing the sea, of sleeping in a big white bed smelling of lavender, in a stone-floored room with heavy shutters. I picture myself healthy again, with long hair, marrying Andreas in a garden planted high with sunflowers. In my darkened room I play music, the same tracks over and over. Songs from my *Buddha Bar* CD with names like 'Solo por tu Amor' and 'Tango

Serenato de Schubert.' They transport me to far-away places, to long evenings in gardens scented with orange blossom and jasmine and filled with the sway of music and bodies, of nights spent dancing and flirting.

My daydreams may carry me on exotic adventures but my body tells me otherwise. It feels plundered. By the surgery, the drugs, the hair loss. Desire can exist only in my mind. But despite this, there's still a part of me that longs to have someone wrap their arms tightly around me, to feel the softness of boundaries blurring rather than always the hard edges of my own form.

The following evening is Paola's hen night, arranged long before we knew my chemo schedule would be put back. She's booked a table at Manna and I make myself go along for a bit. Tonight, their food tastes like metal.

Out of the five of us I'm the only one who's not married or about to be. And, apart from Paola, the only one without a baby. I get a real why me moment, remembering the all of us at school together. Where did I go wrong? Inevitably, there's quite a bit of children talk. Paola shoots me an apologetic glance as Melissa and Ayala talk about breastfeeding.

'So, what's happening with that guy you met at the party?' asks Catherine.

It's now almost three weeks since I saw Andreas. I'm confused by the nice things he said like visiting Stockholm together and meeting again soon, combined with the lack of a follow-up call. My friends don't say, *He hasn't called so he's probably not interested.* Instead, they suggest I contact him.

Too shy to call, I text Andreas the next day. I rewrite the message a few times, trying to get the tone right. *Hi, hope all's good with you. Wondering if you'd like to catch up again? Annabel.*

He replies the same day. *Sounds good. How about Weds or Thurs next week? A.* I re-read his message, trying to gauge his keenness.

We meet at The Oak, a beautifully renovated Victorian pub in Notting Hill.

'You look lovely,' says my mother as I leave the house. I've told her I'm meeting Ioana, so she seems a little surprised by my tight black trousers, high-heeled boots and makeup.

Andreas and I sit close together at a corner table, hands almost touching. Like last time, conversation's easy.

'Do you know what you want from your life?' he asks when we're on our second drink.

Right now, having a long one would be enough, but I concoct some worthy-sounding ambitions about doing meaningful social or public architecture rather than just beauty spas and expensive houses.

'I know exactly how you feel. The time I built a playground for some kids in south London was one of the most satisfying things I've ever done. I felt as if I'd really contributed.' Of course, this makes me like him even more.

Later, he walks me back to my car. We move along the street together in silence. It's only early September but the night air already holds the first whisper of autumn. I am conscious of the small gap between our bodies and watch this shape as it oscillates between us. Will it ever disappear? I want him to kiss me, to prove all is not lost.

His lips briefly brush my cheeks. I drive home, disappointed.

I get a text from Andreas on Friday morning. *Guess what - met yr boss Jamie & all yr workmates at an exhib opening last night! Where were u?* Finally, my hidden life is starting to catch up with me.

Had to miss it unfortunately, I text back.

124

He calls on Saturday morning. 'Are you going to Nadia's party tonight?'

'Who's Nadia?'

'What do you mean, who's Nadia! She works in the same office as you! I met her the other day with Jamie.'

Nadia. Of course. A German girl who started there about two weeks before I left.

'Oh, you mean work Nadia. I'd forgotten all about her party as I'm already doing something else.'

'That's a shame. I was really hoping you'd be there. But it'd be great to get together sometime next week.'

Now I'm very confused. He wants to see me next week again already, yet he never called after our first date, and didn't try and kiss me after our second. He seems confident, so it can't be shyness holding him back. Perhaps he's just a slow mover who likes to get to know someone properly first? And what a nice change that would actually make to having someone jump on you as quickly as possible.

I ask Ioana whether she thinks I should just tell him about the cancer. He could have already heard through my colleagues.

'I think he likes you and that he's come into your life for a good reason, perhaps to help you heal. If you tell him, I think he'll like you even more. He'll just want to protect you and look after you.'

We meet up again on the first anniversary of 9/11. On the radio I hear how thousands of white petals will be thrown from the vaults of St Paul's Cathedral, in tribute to those who didn't make it to today.

Andreas and I watch *Talk to Her* by Pedro Almodovar at a cinema near Leicester Square. Two women lie in a coma in a private clinic. One is visited by her boyfriend every day and the other is looked after by a male nurse. A story about sickness and about love. Andreas is leaning slightly forward in his seat, the curve of his spine peeling away from the chair. He's wearing a soft grey sweater. I want to lift my hands from my lap and run them across the contours of his back

'I wish I could make architecture as stunning as that movie,' he says as we leave the cinema. How wonderful it would be to go out with a man who appreciates such bittersweet beauty.

At Bar Italia in Soho, he asks me how work's going.

Is it a trick question? Since having met my boss and workmates and going to Nadia's party, does he know the truth, which is that I haven't actually been there since early May? Is he interested in me or not? And what if he were to try and kiss me, and his hands discovered the hair on my head wasn't in fact real?

'Actually, I haven't been at work much recently.'

He looks surprised.

'I've had to take some time off because I've been ill.'

I pause.

'I've had breast cancer. I mean it was caught very early and they've said I'm going to be absolutely fine. But basically, they make everyone under the age of thirty-five have chemotherapy. So that's why I haven't been at work.'

I try and make it sound as light as possible. I don't want him thinking that because I have cancer I'm dying, and therefore not a very desirable prospect for a girlfriend.

He asks enough questions about it to be polite before moving on to another subject.

'It's getting late,' he says about half an hour later.

We say goodnight outside Tottenham Court Road Station. This is the moment where, under the city lights, he is supposed to take me in his arms, kiss me and tell me how precious I am and he never wants to let me go. Outside the hot dog stall, he briefly hugs me goodnight. I walk down steps strewn with fast food wrappers. Inside the Tube, caressed by its familiar warmth and dirt, I struggle not to cry.

15

Summer is almost at its end. I'm packing up my flat. I've hardly spent any time here over the past few months, coming only occasionally to pick up the post or get some more clothes. I used to love living here. Now, whenever I go into the bedroom I can't help thinking about that April night. These days, the flat smells abandoned. It has a dark musty flavour that won't go away, even when I open the windows.

Soon, the young city solicitor I've never met will fill my space with his life. I'll become one of those other faceless people who once lived here; just a name on some of the envelopes piled up in the hallway.

I'll take my boxes to my parents' house, leaving most of them unopened for the moment. I don't know how long they'll stay there. I'm registered with a few estate agents and occasionally, out of curiosity, I go and see a flat. But right now, everything feels too unsettled to actually consider buying.

On Friday morning, I lock the door for the last time feeling, to my surprise, no sadness or regret. I hand the keys over to the agents and head straight to chemotherapy.

Most of the veins in my right arm and hand have now blown. They glare at me, purple and red, from behind translucent skin. Today, it takes five stabs of the needle to connect into one. 'Try not to be so tense,' the nurse says. It only makes me more so.

'Do you still want the ice cap?'

'Yes - my hair's actually just started coming back.'

I first noticed the dark stubble across my scalp a few days ago. At night and in the mornings, I run my hands across it, loving the rough, gritty feel of the protruding bristles.

'That's very unusual. It doesn't normally come back until about a month after you finish chemo.'

I look at her kind, sensible face and decide not to mention the healing.

Chris comes over after chemo. I'm hoping he can ease the sickness like he did before.

That night I'm sick, but only twice. When my phone bleeps the next morning, I assume it's Chris, checking in to see how I am, as he always does the day after a session.

How did it all go? Let me know when you're ready for our next get-together. A.

And I thought I'd never hear from Andreas again. But he cares, he even wants to see me. On a day where all I can do is lie in bed nauseous, the hours always pass very slowly. So when I try and call him back just five hours later, it feels to me as if I've left a decent margin between his text and my response. I get his voicemail.

When after a couple of days he hasn't called back, I try and get strict with myself:

Be realistic. If there was something there, he'd have called back by now.

But, I counteract, Maybe he's not quite sure what to do – if someone you quite liked suddenly told you they had cancer, you'd probably be a bit scared, too.

He does call. Five days later.

'I'm so sorry. Things have been really crazy at work. How are you now?' We chat for over half an hour, the conversation broken by me, because I have to go out.

'Do you want to catch up this weekend?' he asks.

I tell him I'm going to Rome for a friend's wedding. We arrange to meet the following week.

Once again, I'm confused. He texts straight after chemo, yet takes days to calls back. Then chats for ages and wants to see me almost immediately. What is he trying to say?

My hotel room in Rome is dominated by an orange carpet and matching bedspread. Two of its walls are lined in mirrored cupboards with gold handles. The street outside is so narrow that I can almost touch the window opposite mine. At night, I draw the curtains tightly before removing my wig. The mirrored doors reflect my head from different angles and I look curiously at my profile against my slowly darkening scalp.

Lots of people I know from London have come to the wedding. It's perfect late September weather and not so long ago this would have been the kind of weekend I'd have loved: wandering around one of the most beautiful cities in the world, a big group of us going out for dinner and then on to a bar on the Friday night. Saturday lunch in a restaurant off Piazza Navona, filled with Italian families. But this weekend, I find all the rushing around and late nights exhausting rather than exhilarating. For the first time, I slightly regret still pretending, to most people, to be the same as everyone else. Yet I don't want to have to be singled out as the one who's different.

Paola and Costas's wedding ceremony is in Sant'Andrea al Quirinale, a seventeenth century church designed by Bernini. I remember its elliptical shaped plan and gold and stucco dome from our first-year architecture field trip here in 1990.

I'm wearing a pink top and skirt, which Paola helped me choose on one of our mid-week visits to Marylebone High Street. I'd originally wanted to wear the pale blue-grey dress I bought for Tanya and Axel's wedding last summer but it's backless and so cut away that it exposes most of my scar. Today, Tanya's wearing it instead.

'Look at you two sisters, both so glamorous,' my friend Ajay says when we arrive at the church. I have on the same four-inch stiletto sandals I wore to Tanya's wedding. My feet are almost the only part of my body that hasn't changed at all.

After the service, we all walk to a nearby palazzo and drink champagne in the garden before dinner.

'I'm putting you between two of Costas's football friends,' Paola told me. 'They're both single. One's a policeman, the other's a lawyer.'

The policeman is tall and fair, the lawyer, shorter and dark. Both are friendly and quite attractive but I don't sense any particular spark either way. Over dinner, our table starts talking about relationships. Across from me, a stunning dark-haired Greek girl with a large diamond on her ring finger says, 'I think it's about growing to love someone. The more you know a person, the more you can love them. Otherwise, it's just fantasy.'

'I disagree,' says the lawyer. 'You just know when you first meet someone whether you could fall in love with them.'

'What do you think?' the policeman asks me.

'They've both got a point. I think there needs to be something that draws you to someone in the first place, but I also think this idea of love at first sight can be really misleading. You can be incredibly attracted to someone but they may not be able to give you what you need.'

I'm thinking about Andreas as I speak, and how I liked him right from the beginning. Yet I'm finally coming to realise that he doesn't seem to be available for me. It doesn't stop me from still wanting him, though.

I meet up with him a couple of days later. He calls in the morning to tell me a friend of his is having a birthday party at a bar in Parsons Green. 'I know we talked about a movie, but is it OK if we have a bite then head down there?'

Is it a good sign he's taking me with him to a party and introducing me to his friends? Or a bad one that he wouldn't rather spend the whole evening alone with me?

It's the first time we've met since I told him. I'm wearing a low cut, close-fitting top as I want to make it quite clear I still have two breasts. Luckily, I can still do low cut as my scar's across the side of my breast. I don't have much cleavage, but I've always liked low necklines as my neck and collarbones are one of my favourite parts of my body.

'Are you two together?' someone asks me while Andreas is getting us drinks.

'We're just friends.' I try and sound as chilled as possible.

His psychiatrist friend Joachim, who I met at Michael's party, is also there. He's brought his girlfriend Katie. She's friendly but very outgoing and confident and dominates the conversation. Next to her, I feel awkward and tongue-tied.

'Another drink?' Andreas asks me.

'Just a fizzy water, please. I'm not really into alcohol at the moment.'

'I hardly drink myself as you've probably noticed.' He smiles and looks me straight in the eye, 'I don't think you need alcohol to have a romantic time.'

A warm sensation floods my chest. But later, when I drop him off in Notting Hill after the party, he doesn't ask if I want to come in.

'Let's catch that new Mike Leigh film soon.' He waves goodbye. 'I'll give you a call.' I drive home, half thinking about when he might call and also trying to tell myself that I need to realise it's almost certainly not going to happen between us.

Leaves are falling from the trees, cladding the city streets in golds, greens, and oranges. They crackle under my feet. Regent's Park is still steeped in the warmth and light of Indian Summer but people dress differently, walk more briskly and no longer sprawl on the now leaf-carpeted grass.

My mother goes into hospital to have her varicose veins removed. The roles of carer and cared for are briefly reversed. I drive her there and stay with her while the nurses and the anaesthetist ask all the same questions I was asked in May.

She calls after the surgery, still half asleep, remote. When I see her again she's lying in bed, groggy, hers legs bandaged, her face lined and tired. I sit with her for an hour and in the quiet of late afternoon I remember how it was also around this time of day when she first arrived at the hospital to see me.

Today, I look at her and realise she's not always the invincible one. She's seventy-one and it's actually possible she could be closer to the end of her life than I am. For months, I've assumed it would be the other way round.

It's October. Pink Ribbon month. Newspapers and magazines are crammed with breast cancer stories: heroic ones of its survivors, tragic ones of its victims. I read them all and get scared by ones which, like my own, began with a relatively optimistic prognosis before the cancer returned. Seeing these, it can be hard not to assume my fate will be the same. I have to keep reminding myself that there are no fixed rules to this illness and that my story is my own.

In mid-October, I have my final session of chemotherapy. The night before, I dream I am locked in a wire cage in the middle of a vast flat field. I can see for miles across it and long to be released.

I always see Dr Jones immediately before chemotherapy. She asks how I am, whether I've had any side effects and checks my breasts. This time, I ask her to check my right breast very carefully as over the last few days I've repeatedly felt a hard area just below the skin. It does feel different to the tumour, but I've lost sense of what's normal and what's not.

She runs her fingers slowly across it. 'This is completely normal breast tissue. I think you're just premenstrual.'

Premenstrual. A word I used to dislike so much.

'I get scared, though. Is it ever going to go away?'

'It's completely normal, especially as it's still very early days. It'll lessen with time. I've also noticed that whenever there are a lot of news stories about breast cancer, like at the moment, or when someone famous dies of it, everyone's anxiety levels seem to go up. I sometimes wonder whether the media does more harm than good to my patients.'

By now, just being in the treatment room is enough to make me feel sick and I start retching as soon as I walk in. The first time I was here, I was able to register its architecture; the high ceilings, cornicing, ceiling rose, panelled doors. Now I am left with just a landscape of needles and drip bags.

The nurses always used to check my white blood cell count the day before. My veins are now so fragile, they don't want to have to put the needle in twice so I'm having the blood test just before the treatment instead. The nurse leaves the canula in, bandages up my right hand and tells me to come back in an hour when the results will be ready.

I walk over to Marylebone High Street. It's a chilly Friday lunchtime and people are submerged within the warmth of cafes, or walk swiftly along the pavements, faintly euphoric as it's almost the weekend. I go into Starbucks, order a herbal tea and sit in an armchair. The red-haired receptionist from the oncology unit comes in with the man who serves the sandwiches in the chemo room. They sit down on a nearby sofa, but don't notice me. I watch them giggle and flirt over coffees.

As soon as the treatment begins, I start vomiting. The nurse places an army green screen around me. 'Talk to me about anything but this,' she says. She's new, young and pretty with bleached hair. I ask if she's got any holidays planned. 'No – I had to take some time off work as I was ill and I've only just come back.' I don't ask what was wrong.

After ten minutes, I throw off the ice cap, not caring if I lose the little hair I've got.

I'm crying when I hug the nurses goodbye. It's forever, I hope.

16

'There's a clinic in Holland you should consider visiting once chemo's finished,' suggested the glamorous doctor who gives me the vitamin infusions. 'They do a water therapy treatment that'll help you detox from it.' She gave me a leaflet and told me to speak to Emma, the woman with ovarian cancer. She'd already been once and wanted to go back.

Mr Essaidi has developed a novel non-invasive therapeutic technology to effectively inhibit the action of surplus radicals and to reduce their synthesis. The entire treatment takes place in the Essaidi cabin, in which the parameters, such as temperature, pressure, light intensity and energy volume are precisely regulated and strictly controlled by a computerised system.

It sounded bizarre. I ask Emma how she found it, and tell her I'm considering going in mid-October.

'Great - I was full of energy after. I've even been able to go to the gym again.'

'We could go together,' she suggests. 'You're supposed to have a companion with you for the treatment. My husband came last time, but it's difficult as they're only open in the week. He's already had to take so much time off work 'cos of me.'

'Sure.' I'm grateful not to have to go there alone, but hoping she's not going to have to actually come into the treatment cabin with me. I don't want this woman I hardly know to see my scarred, naked body.

We meet at Stansted on Tuesday at lunchtime. Today, I don't have the sense of excitement airports usually induce in me. Our Ryanair flights to Eindhoven cost £1.99 and when we arrive, I understand why. Driving through the city, we pass through street after street of repetitive high-rise sixties buildings. They remind me of the post-war concrete boulevards in East Berlin.

'The city is the global headquarters of Philips Electrics and has the densest concentration of high-tech industry in the Netherlands,' says our cab driver. He turns away from its centre and the buildings become smaller, the streets more leafy. We head into a long curving drive lined with sycamores. The ground is green and lush, sodden with recent rainfall. Towards the horizon, I see the dense canopy of a forest. At the end of the drive, the cab stops outside a low-slung building.

Several people, most of them wearing only dressing gowns, are sitting on the black leather sofas in the large reception area. It's chilly, even inside. Large fixed glass windows frame the landscape, a thin membrane between us and this damp autumn afternoon.

We're handed robes and told to get changed and wait. I notice a very beautiful woman, probably in her sixties, curled up on one of the sofas. What has brought her here? The treatment's also supposed to be good for anti-ageing, but she's so skinny I can't decide whether she's very sick or very image conscious. In a world where you can apparently never be too thin, there's sometimes an almost invisible line between the two. Others' situations are more obvious: a man in a wheelchair, a woman almost carried along on the arm of a concerned-looking husband.

We wait for a long time. I'd never be this late for a client. Do they think ill people have nothing better to do with their time? I'm annoyed, even though it's not as if there's anything I particularly want to do in Eindhoven.

Nearly an hour later, my name is called out for a consultation with the doctor. He speaks only Dutch.

'He says you must not worry,' his interpreter tells me. 'You come here perhaps six times and we cure your tumours.'

Cure my tumours.

'Have you not read my form? I've already had surgery to remove the tumour and as far as I'm aware I don't have any active cancer.'

The doctor looks on blankly on while I speak, chubby hairy fingers tapping his pen on the table.

'Oh, I am very sorry indeed for the misunderstanding. As you can see, we really are terribly busy today.'

If I hadn't travelled all this way, I would leave now.

Instead, I go into one of the four private cabins. Luckily, they are so busy they've forgotten to make any mention of the 'companion.' And Emma's nowhere to be seen, so I presume she's also, thankfully, having a solo treatment.

A female voice crackles through the tannoy.

'Please remove all clothes and jewellery and take a shower before entering the treatment area. Press the red button on the wall when you are ready to begin.'

I go in. All the walls and the ceiling are lined in mirrors. It smells of swimming pool changing rooms. I press the button.

'Please lie down on the bed and your treatment will begin.'

The bed is covered in grey vinyl, its surface cool and sticky under my skin. Coloured lights start flashing, hisses and grunts emanate from somewhere, and lukewarm water intermittently rains down from a contraption above me.

I gaze up at my reflection floating on the ceiling. An almost hairless, naked body, pale white under the artificial lights.

When I first heard about the Essaidi cabin, I pictured a warm timber-lined space, smelling of something therapeutic like rosemary or juniper. But this room and this treatment are cold and impersonal and I can't wait for it to be over.

After fifteen long minutes the lights, sounds and water suddenly stop. The disembodied voice returns. 'Please take another shower and repeat then exactly the same procedure.'

The Eindhoven Holiday Inn is an eleven-storey concrete slab, fronted by a barren windy piazza.

From the eighth-floor room Emma and I are sharing, I look down through a narrow strip of glass, which won't open. The city is now veiled in a light drizzle through which the glimmer of a sun recedes. Beneath me, dotted trails of light move as people cycle home. High up in this sad, ghost-like city, I feel so far away from everyone who matters. I miss my mother, even though I only saw her this morning.

I check my mobile for messages, half hoping Andreas might have left one about going to the cinema. He hasn't, even though it's been almost two weeks since we last met. Forget him, I tell myself.

There are times when it's lonelier to be with people than to be alone. This evening, I wish I could just escape into my book and forget where I am.

'Shall we go down and have a drink before dinner?' Emma suggests.

Surrounded by conference delegates laughing, smoking and ordering bottle after bottle of wine, we sit drinking mineral water, our conversation increasingly punctuated by silences as we run out of things to talk about.

I look at the menu. It's almost all meat, which I haven't had in months. Suddenly, I want it. I order pigeon breast followed by venison.

We turn in early. We each know the other's wearing a wig, but we get into bed and turn the lights off, our wigs still on our heads. In the darkness, I quietly remove mine before going to sleep.

In the middle of the night, I wake up feeling sick. I rush to the bathroom and vomit several times. After, I flush the toilet, hoping I haven't disturbed Emma. I brush my teeth but the gamey taste of the meat still lingers.

I can't get back to sleep. The alarm clock on the bedside table spells out *04.38* in fluorescent green dashes. I lie in bed as the dashes slowly change, and an autumn dawn gradually filters through the thin orange curtains.

06.34 and Emma's still sleeping. In the half-light, I can see she's also removed her wig. I look away, and put mine back on before getting out of bed.

She's awake when I come out of the shower, her wig on her head. I don't mention being sick in the night.

Downstairs, I order peppermint tea to soothe my stomach. It's only just gone seven but the dining room's almost full. Everyone else sits there with shiny leather briefcases, tables piled with croissants, ham and cheese pastries, pots of coffee. The people next to us are discussing their latest deals and plans: 'I'm in Barcelona tomorrow, Cyprus the day after and New York next week,' says one man. Such busy, busy lives. I am both envious at their apparent purposefulness and relieved not to have to rush around like that.

Back at the clinic, without enthusiasm, I repeat the same process as yesterday. After, I feel empty, as if everything's been drained out of me. Emma tells me she feels really good. 'It's given me that burst of energy again.'

By now I find the chilly waiting area with its black leather sofas and sick-looking people decidedly creepy. I can't wait to get out.

Our flight's not until three so we go back into the city centre. I eat cheese on toast in a crowded warm café with steamed-up windows, relieved to be back in the normal world. Then we wander round the rainy, almost deserted pedestrian streets in the central shopping precinct, moving from shop to shop, pretending to be interested in clumsy shoes and handbags.

My phone bleeps. Chris. *Where r u? Was trying to tune into yr energy & send u some remote healing, but I can't find u anywhere…x*

Good to hear u, I text back. *In Holland having weird post chemo supposed detox treatment. Home soon thank god x*

'So, what have you two been doing in Eindhoven?' We're in a taxi going back to the airport.

'We've been to the Essaidi Clinic,' Emma says. 'Do you know it?'

'Isn't that where they do some strange water thing? It's supposed to be able to cure even cancer. But why were you two there?'

I speak before Emma has a chance. 'We're beauty journalists from *Vogue* magazine in London. We're researching a feature on anti-ageing treatments. The clinic's water therapy is also supposed to be excellent for that.'

I've been away for just over a day but I'm so happy when the plane's wheels hit the tarmac at Stansted.

On my way home from Liverpool Street Station, I watch my city slide past me in the Wednesday afternoon rain and already fading light, feeling only affection for the traffic jam on Great Eastern Street, the mirrored office building at Old Street roundabout, and the fried chicken shops opposite King's Cross Station.

17

In the gap between finishing chemotherapy and starting radiotherapy, Tanya and I decide to take a short trip together. Now it's truly autumn, I'd love to be in a warm house in the country. I imagine log fires, roll top baths, old wood floors and crisp white linen, somewhere with massages and earthy food.

I search the Internet, but nothing seems to quite match the image I have. The spa hotels are all big and impersonal with floral bedrooms and grand dining rooms serving nouvelle cuisine diet food. Babington House, in Somerset, would be perfect except it's two hundred pounds upwards a night just for a room and breakfast, and will probably be filled with glamorous media couples.

Eventually, I find somewhere in Ireland, west of Dublin. Temple Spa is in a Georgian house, owned by the same family for generations. As well as treatments, they have yoga and walks. They also grow most of their own food. I book us a three-day mid-week package.

It's raining when we land. We're the only passengers on the bus to Horseleap. It rattles its way out of the city centre, miles of suburbs eventually giving way to a straight road, which cuts through a flat landscape of farmland scattered with small towns.

There's a stillness to this place. From my bedroom window, I see only fields, cows and sky. Our deal was for a double room but my sister persuaded them to let us have two singles for almost the same price. She goes to bed late and gets up late and I'm the opposite. I like having my own space while knowing she's only the other side of the wall.

As part of our package, we're offered a free hydrotherapy bath. The receptionist hands me a questionnaire to fill in. 'You'll need to go through this with the head therapist before you have any treatments.'

Describe any surgery carried out in the past twelve months.

'But you're so young, my love.' The therapist is in her fifties and I know she's trying to be kind. People often tell me I'm *too young* for this illness. But it actually makes me feel as if there's something really flawed with me for having got it so early.

'Have you had any other treatment apart from the surgery?'

When she hears I've just finished chemo, she tells me the hydrotherapy is too intense for my system at the moment. She suggests reflexology instead, which I like. But, still, I wish I could just be like everyone else.

In the evening, the rain pauses. We walk across the courtyard to the main house for dinner. It's almost pitch black, the moon hidden by clouds. Gravel crunches underfoot and the sharp night air holds the smell of smoke and cow dung.

There are twelve of us staying and we all eat dinner round a polished mahogany table in a room filled with family antiques and silver. The others are mostly Irish, and older. It's more like being at a dinner party than in a hotel. A rotund German psychologist and his Irish wife, who live in Cork, keep us entertained with stories of their recent trip to a weight loss spa in Austria where they were given just one hard bread roll for breakfast, and told to chew it fifty times before swallowing.

'Zis is much better value.' He tucks into his roast lamb and red wine.

That night, I sleep well for the first time in weeks.

It is a relief to be surrounded by the silence and spaciousness of the landscape. It rains most of the time, in long slanted sheets. I spend a lot of time in my room, often just staring out of the window and watching the clouds drift across the sky. Sometimes Tanya joins me and we sit on my bed chatting or reading.

'I'm thinking of going back to university,' she tells me. 'To do a science degree.' My eyes widen. At school, I hated science. It fascinates me how alike yet unalike we are. We share the same voices, gestures, walk, hair (though in different colours) and sense of humour. Yet our minds and our faces are so different. I was terrible at music and she hated writing essays. She's fair with a turned-up nose and full lips and I'm dark with a Roman nose and a more angular face. When people first meet us, they often can't believe we're sisters.

I'm exhausted. Now chemo's over, I'm like a spring that's suddenly gone slack. I try a yoga class and a short walk but all I really want to do is sit by the fire, slide into my bed, or lie on a massage table.

On our last afternoon, I have reflexology with a woman called Mary. I've had more alternative treatments in the last few months than the rest of my life put together.

Mary talks all the way through.

'You know, God only lets it happen to those who are strong enough...everything in life happens for a reason...you're so lucky to have been through this so young. You'll have so much time to put the wisdom it's given you to good use...I can just tell, you're going to have such a wonderful life.'

Her words make me hopeful, especially spoken in that soothing Irish accent. But I also know that lots of people who get cancer don't have happy endings, and that unfortunately life is not always fair.

18

I return to the oncology unit to be measured up for radiotherapy. A nurse leads me through a maze of brightly lit, white basement corridors, whose low ceilings seem to press down on my head. We go into a white room dominated by a large white machine with a treatment bed attached to it. I've always thought of white as a good colour: pure and clean, able to make a space feel lighter and bigger. But here, under the artificial light, it feels clinical and cold.

'Strip off to the waist,' the nurse tells me and stays in the room. By now I'm so used to this instruction that getting undressed in front of strangers no longer makes me self-conscious.

Once I'm lying on the bed, a male nurse joins us. He walks straight over to the machine, barely glancing at my naked torso. 'We'll be taking some scans with the simulator today, which we'll use to design your treatment.'

During my second preparatory appointment, the female nurse tells me that they'll need to tattoo three black dots onto my skin. 'They'll provide us with locating points each time the machine's set up for your treatment. You'll have one between your breasts and one on each side.'

I ask whether they can come off when the treatment's over.

'No, they're permanent. Don't worry they're only tiny, about a millimetre in diameter each - you'll hardly see them.'

The tattooing feels like a small pinprick. It's a lot less painful than being injected for chemo. At home, I go straight to the mirror. They are small but, at least to my eyes, visible. I try on a low-cut top and the black mark in the centre of my cleavage glares back at me. Would a man notice it?

I remember the nurse's no-nonsense voice and her underlying tone. *Don't make a fuss about something which, in the bigger picture of cancer, is so incredibly trivial.* When I think that I could be dead, or could have secondaries, or could have no breasts, she's right, it is trivial. But I am tired of living by the standards of this world, where it's so often implied that I ought to consider myself lucky. Because when I put myself back in the other world, the one which until six months ago was the only one I knew, I am not so lucky.

Chris comes over to give me some healing.

'There's someone I've been thinking about setting you up with. He's a client - Swedish but lives in Dubai. Your energies could work well together. Can I pass on your email?'

'Is he hot?'

'Well, obviously I can't judge myself. But I think women find him attractive.'

'OK, I'll give it a try.'

Towards the end of our session, he says to me, 'I'd like a girlfriend. Do you have any nice friends you could introduce me to?'

'They're all nice but I'm not sure they're your type. There's one you could try, though. Tall, thin, blonde & gorgeous. With a sexy Romanian accent.' It sounds like I'm trying to sell her on E-Bay.

'Brilliant, I like foreign birds. Can you give me her number?'

'She's one of my best friends, not some bird.'

'You know I'm only kidding.'

147

'Why not,' says Ioana, when I suggest introducing her to Chris.

Had long chat, he texts me two days later. *Loved her accent. Meeting next Tues. Quite excited! x*

The Sunday before the date, Kwong invites me and Ioana over for supper. He's making Chinese, his speciality. Poor Kwong. I haven't told him anything about what's been happening but I have given him strict instructions over what I will and won't eat. I've told him I'm doing a special detox programme 'to clean out my system' and can't have meat or dairy, and that he has to make brown rice and if possible, everything should be organic.

I must sound like a complete princess. One part of me thinks, just tell him for God's sake, while another defiantly says no, why should I. We get on really well, but I haven't known him that long and he's someone I usually just go out to parties with, rather than share my inner world with.

While we're eating our tofu and broccoli stir-fry, Ioana gets a text.

Driving back from seeing my daughter in Devon. Really looking forward to Tuesday xx

'Who's this guy, then?' asks Kwong.

'Someone Annabel set me up with.' Ioana is primed not to give too much away.

'How do you know him?'

I keep it vague. 'He's kind of a family friend and looking for a girlfriend. I thought they could check each other out.'

Ioana calls on Wednesday morning.

'So, how did it go?'

'Pretty good. He seems really nice.'

'Where did you meet?'

'At a wine bar near Liverpool Street Station.'

'What do you reckon?'

'Not bad at all.' She pauses. 'And I think he quite liked me. He's already asked what I'm doing this weekend.'

An email arrives from Dubai:

> *Hi Yeah,*
> *Got your name and email from Chris. Guess he has told you about me. I live in Dubai and work as a product dude. Actually, I'm the marketing manager for Sony Ericsson-extremely fun. How about yourself? What do you do for a living, where do you live, how do you know Chris, what kind of a person are you, what makes you happy, what makes you sad, what do you look like, what about your family, what do you like doing, hate doing...wow the list is long, give it a shot!*
> *Like to hear from you,*
> *Best regards,*
> *Vincent*

I respond, feeding him the story about how I'm an architect working for a cool design practice, and how I have my own flat.

His reply arrives just a few hours later. It is two pages long. Is he sending me a standard girlfriend-hunting text? It outlines his life story and philosophy, describing at great length how as a child in Sweden his parents refused to buy him a dog so he spent three years saving up all his pocket money and doing odd jobs so he could buy one himself.

> *...The whole process of this shaped me. I set my mind on something I want to do and become extremely focused and no one can stop me until I get to my goal...OK so here comes my next list of questions!!! Which company do you*

149

work for; do you have a mobile, what make and model (and your number please!!!)? Address? Can you email a photo of yourself? What do you want to do in the next few years? How do you cope with challenges in your life? What do you want to do with your life? How have your relationships been? Had any lately?

I deliberately take a few days to reply.

Hi Vincent,
Thanks for your long email. Very interesting to hear about the dog. You do ask a lot of questions! You might not agree but I can't help finding email a poor substitute for meeting in person, which I think is the only way you can tell whether two people might get on. I could tell you my life story and send a photo but then we could meet and I might be totally different from what you expect, or vice versa. So anyway, you say you come to London quite often so why don't we have a coffee next time you're over.
Best wishes,
Annabel

Hi Annabel,
Right, yeah, cool I think you may have a point. So basically what you're saying is either you get on a plane to Dubai or I get on a plane to London. It's warm and sunny here and we have beautiful beaches. How soon do you think you could get out?
Really looking forward to hearing from you.
Vincent

No Vincent, I am not saying that at all. Didn't you read my last email? ...*a coffee next time you're over.* Anyway, my six weeks of daily radiotherapy begin tomorrow so I certainly won't be getting on any planes to Dubai.

19

Just as I'm about to leave the house for my first radiotherapy appointment, someone from the oncology unit calls. 'Afraid the machine's broken down so you won't be able to come today. Come at half six-tomorrow evening instead.' Cancer machines, it seems, are no different to Tube trains and builders' vans.

The building's almost deserted when I arrive. There's no one at reception and most of the lights are off. Feeling like an intruder, I move through the silent corridor and down the stairwell.

In the basement, there's one other person waiting. A woman in her fifties, her bright green coat, red lipstick and long blonde hair incongruous with the surroundings. Can the hair be real? She starts chatting. It turns out she's an actress.

'I've got another couple of weeks of this to go then I'm starting in the Christmas pantomime at the Chichester rep. Are you being treated for breast cancer, too?'

'I am. I just finished chemo. This is my first radio session.'

'But you're so lucky. You didn't lose your hair.'

I'm impressed at how good my wig is, if even those who have reason to suspect my hair's not real can't tell.

'Oh, but I did and how. I've just been able to disguise it well. How about you?'

'Every last strand. I've bought myself three different wigs. Long blonde, bobbed black and short red. It's been quite fun.'

A nurse comes to get me. We go down a short ramped corridor and into the large white room with the white machine in the middle.

I lie half naked on the bed as two nurses adjust the angle of the radiotherapy machine, one instructing the other.

'Lovely...just a little over to the right, Katie...great, almost there...perfect.'

'We're going to leave now,' the nurse who's in charge tells me. 'The first round takes sixty seconds. Then we'll readjust it for the next one. That's only thirty seconds. You can breathe normally but just make sure you keep completely still.'

They dim the lights and go out. The machine makes a grunting noise and starts to move, tracing an arc across my body with its giant white arm. Five minutes later, I'm back outside.

I've heard others say they found having a machine hovering above them alienating and impersonal, and that they preferred chemotherapy because at least there was some human contact. But I love the way it always retains a space between us. Lying in the semi darkness, listening to it whirring across me, is oddly soothing.

'What do you think about while you're lying there, love?' a nurse asks one day. 'Bet you're doing your Christmas shopping lists in your head.'

'Something like that.'

Actually, I am trying to imagine that my left breast is part of an ancient sculpture made of white Carrera marble. The machine is cleaning it up, removing all the traces of dirt and grit, which have become embedded in it over the years. In the end, it'll be perfect again.

The vibrant colours of autumn fade into winter. London is muffled in pewter. The leaves in the park are now crisp and translucent, their veins protruding and their once gold, green, and orange tones now drained to a dull copper. They cover the black November earth. Above, empty branches sigh against a liquid sky.

The basement waiting area at the oncology unit always smells of stale coffee and damp wool, mixed with the chemical smell I have come to associate with this building. It's an intimate space, just the section of corridor that links the staircase to the treatment rooms. Two tight lines of chairs are pressed up against each wall allowing just enough room to pass through. Beneath the glare of the lights, we sit together and wait for our appointments. I see the same faces again and again.

Some look down at their feet, or hide behind a newspaper, awkward at how we are all compressed into this space. One woman wears her sunglasses every day. An American woman spends all her time on the phone to the office, brisk and efficient, using potentially wasted minutes. Almost every day I see a tall thin man reading *The Financial Times*. He wears polished brogues and a perfectly pressed grey suit with a silk handkerchief in the breast pocket. But his suit's much too big and he always looks pale and tired. It's OK not to pretend everything's fine, I long to say to him.

Others, such as myself, prefer to acknowledge this common ground we all share. Several of the women I talk to also have breast cancer. Most are at least middle aged. When I get chatting to one, who must be in her sixties, my first thought is poor her, she's still pretty young to get it. Then I realise she's easily double the age I am. Right now, if someone told me I had thirty cancer-free years ahead of me, I'd be thrilled.

Another says casually, 'I'm on me third bout of breast cancer in five years,' as if she were describing the flu. A third tells me how she lives outside London and it's quite fun having to come in every day as it means she gets to do lots of shopping. 'I've bought myself seven pairs of shoes since I started radio three weeks ago.'

There's only one woman around my age. She often brings her two young daughters and mum with her. She asks how I'm finding the treatment.

'It's so easy compared to chemo.'

'Which one did you have?'

'*FEC*'

'I had that first-time round, too,' she says, the words *first time round* spiking uncomfortably into me. 'I was absolutely fine on it. *Adrymycin,* the one I'm on at the moment, is awful, though.'

'When did you have the *FEC?*'

'Just over a year ago. I thought that was the end of it. But three months ago, it came back. They found it in the lymph nodes in my neck. Unfortunately, the prognosis isn't as good this time. I'm having radio and chemo together at the moment.'

She pulls down her polo neck to show me her throat, painted bright red by the treatment and tells me how she's on a liquid diet as she can't swallow any more. While we chat, her blonde daughters play on the floor with some toys the nurse has brought them, and her mum just keeps smiling.

For the first couple of weeks, I don't mind going to the oncology unit every day. Then it starts to get me down. I'm tired of being surrounded by cancer and constantly seeing people who aren't well. One day, in the waiting area I notice a hairless Middle Eastern guy who can only be in his early twenties. A nurse sits down next to him and I overhear her quietly say, 'We've just had your scans back and I'm afraid the news isn't good. We're going to need to admit you to the ward.' I look at him and feel like crying. He just nods helplessly, his resignation even more painful to watch than tears or anger.

I was warned radiotherapy might make me very tired. The treatments are so quick and uneventful that at first I found this hard to believe. Some people have to travel two hours each way for treatment. They'd have every reason to be tired, but it's only a short drive from my parents' house to Harley Street.

The first two weeks go well. Then exhaustion starts to set in, stubbornly wedging itself into every cell. Like a magnet, gravity pulls my body down, drawing it towards the softness of beds and sofas. Most afternoons I fall asleep, waking up groggy to a winter twilight.

My body is changing. I miss its angular lines, the one gift of my chemo purges. Since finishing it, I've put back on all the weight I lost plus more, despite still being on a healthy diet. My left breast has turned bright red and is so sore I can no longer sleep on that side. It looks and feels like very bad sunburn. In London, in November. And since starting radiotherapy, my nose continuously weeps, there's an eczema-like rash on my face and the asthma, which used to trouble me only rarely, is back. It's winter and I'm sleeping with the window open, but I still wake up in the middle of the night drenched with sweat.

I ask the breast-care nurse if any of these symptoms could have been caused by the radiotherapy. 'Only the tiredness and the red skin around the treated area,' she states. Another woman overhears our conversation and tells us how she's also had a rash and a runny nose since starting the treatment. 'Just coincidence,' the nurse tells us firmly.

The days pass so slowly. I've lost the desire to do much at all and am just counting how many left to go until the end of this. Over the summer, while I was having chemo, I swung between feeling very sick and reasonably well. Now I am constantly tired and not quite right.

I tell myself I ought to be making the most of every moment, not just waiting for time to pass. For if cancer teaches you anything, it's that time is precious and finite and each day should be savoured. But I simply can't be bothered. I give up on meditation and yoga and get into daytime TV, crossword puzzles and trash novels instead.

I'm not going out much anymore. Friends often visit me at home. Julieann, who I've known since my first week at university, turns up most weekends. She's famous for her unreliability and her work as a hotel designer takes her all over the world. We can go for months without seeing one another, so I'm really touched by her steadfast appearances. Since I've been ill, she's been to fifteen different countries including Turkey, Ghana, and Thailand. On these quiet winter afternoons, she's happy to just come to my parents' house and chat. We make an incongruous pair. I'm usually in yoga trousers and a thick jumper and she, just about the most glamorous person I know, usually shows up in a silk jersey wrap dress.

I make it over to Anat's for supper one evening. I love the way she always remembers exactly what I do and don't eat these days. She's made organic teriyaki salmon with roast sweet potatoes and green beans in a delicious dressing with soya sauce and sesame seeds. Usually, just eating her food, gossiping and hanging out in her beautifully pared-down architect's flat with the white painted floorboards makes me very content. Tonight, it doesn't happen.

'I know it's hard at the moment,' she says. 'But I promise that one day you'll be happy again.'

The fear is also back. It sings me its song. *Don't you forget this is an incurable disease and all this treatment will buy you is a bit of time.* It leaps with glee at any hint of pain or discomfort in my body, working its black magic powers of transformation on me. A cough becomes lung cancer. A pain in my hip, bone cancer.

My hip pain lasts about a week. I'm constantly aware of it, along with a sick acid taste in the back of my throat. I hear Dr

Jones saying, *I'm so sorry but there's nothing more we can give you.* And one morning I wake up and it's gone and suddenly I remember how, in the past, that hip used to occasionally play up.

Tanya takes me to a concert of Bach Cantatas at the Wigmore Hall. She's always going to classical concerts and often asks me to join her. I go only occasionally, usually for choral music. Bach and Mozart are my favourites. In the programme notes, I read how the common theme of these is a longing for death, envisaged as more beautiful and pure than life. I doubt Tanya realised. I follow the English translation, my eyes turned down towards the programme, hoping my sister and the stranger on my other side won't notice the tears.

I eagerly await my death;
Ah, if only it were already at hand!
Then I shall escape all the woe
That has kept me bound to the world.

I want life, not death. I've never even questioned this. But as I listen to the music and sense the weariness, the sadness that now weigh me down, something inside me slackens. What if there were some truth to these words? What if I could just stop caring so much about wanting to stay alive?

I don't know what happens when we die, and whether something might lie beyond life. In some cultures, death is thought to be not the final exit point, just the entry into another level of awareness. It's a comforting thought. In a recent therapy session, I asked Javier, a practising Catholic, what he believed.

'I really enjoy my life, but I'm not afraid of dying. I imagine it'll be like falling into the arms of the greatest lover of all.'

I wish I could feel the same.

In early December, I go for my first check up at the surgeon's. I look at the five other women waiting for mammograms and wonder who's had the disease and who hasn't. Impossible to tell.

I pick up *The Times* from the coffee table and try to read an article about Iraq, but my eyes are only skimming over the shapes made by the words, while my brain can't help but preoccupy itself with the fact that I actually have no idea what's going on beneath my skin and that in just a few minutes the machine could discover something I really don't want to be there. It makes me feel so vulnerable.

The woman who did my mammograms back in May is here again today. I remember how she kept breezily saying *All right pet* at the end of each sentence and how much it irritated me.

Today, she redeems herself,

'You know I had cancer when I was about your age.' She compresses the machine over my breast. 'That was over twenty years ago and I've been fine ever since. All right pet. We get all sorts in here, ducky. Far too many your age. Lots of celebrities, too.' Her voice is conspiratorial as she unscrews the plates that have been painfully squashing my breast. 'Them ones all over *Hello*. You'd never guess they'd had cancer.'

The surgeon gives me my results the following day.

'I'm delighted to say everything looks clear. You're doing really well.'

He pauses.

'Now we need to talk about that other lump, the one we found on your right side in May. It's still there. Hasn't grown or anything. But I think you should seriously consider having it out.'

'Why?' My body is suddenly cold, despite the warmth of the gas fire.

'It's incredibly rare, but it has been known for a cancerous tumour to hide behind a benign one. Given your history, I just don't think we should take any chances.'

I remember his words just before my first operation. *Don't worry, it definitely isn't cancer.* Back then, I wasn't scared.

'We can do it in January when all your other treatment's over.' He opens a large black leather-bound diary.

2003. It was meant to be a new start.

20

Radiotherapy was supposed to finish today, the Friday before Christmas, but the machine broke down again yesterday so they had to cancel. I should've had what'll now be my penultimate session this morning, but there's such a backlog they told me to come in the afternoon instead.

It's a weekend of weddings. Today, Kate's in Greenwich. Tomorrow, Patrick and Claudia's in Clerkenwell. I've never been invited to so many weddings as this year. I love watching my friends get married, though there's also an undercurrent of will it ever happen to me?

I'll have to go straight to Greenwich from radiotherapy so I arrive at the oncology unit wearing a chocolate satin skirt, high heels and lots of makeup to try and hide my exhaustion.

'You look so glam,' the nurse says. 'Where are you off to?'

'A friend's wedding.'

'I hope it'll be you next. Make sure you catch that bouquet.'

It's hard to believe that only last year Kate and I were sharing the experience of being single girls in London. We studied architecture together, lived round the corner from each other and both worked for practices in Clerkenwell. We'd regularly cook supper at one of our flats, and at the weekends, we'd often meet to go shopping or to parties and bars.

Last summer, everything changed when she got together with an old school friend.

'I just know he's the one,' she told me only a couple of weeks after it happened. 'It's totally different to anything I've had before.' He was working in San Francisco at the time, so within a few months she left her job, rented out her flat and moved to California. I missed her, but was inspired by her story.

Kate enters the church on her father's arm, a flame-haired winter bride in a cream top and skirt. The first hymn is 'Dear Lord and Father of Mankind,' which always reminds me of my grandmother. Even though I wasn't at all religious, as a child I loved singing hymns with her, and this was our favourite. I remember sitting on a stool in her North Yorkshire kitchen, aged about seven, singing and carefully spooning strawberry jam into the dents cut into her still warm fairy cakes.

We sang this at her funeral fifteen years ago. I sobbed when my dad told me she had cancer. I was sad because I knew she might die, and also because it seemed so unfair that such a gentle and loving person could get such a cruel disease. My sister and I, by then urban teenagers, rarely went to Yorkshire anymore. She'd come to London instead. But I had such happy memories of those childhood visits: arriving into Darlington on the train, knowing she'd be waiting on the platform; the coloured soap pearls she'd drop into my bath; her homemade tomato soup; the delicate watercolours she painted of flowers and animals; her sitting room overlooking fields and sheep.

Kate and Matthew's reception is at Eltham Palace, King Henry VIII's childhood home, in the recently restored Art Deco rooms the Courtauld family created there in the thirties. Lots of people from university are here, some I haven't seen in a decade.

'Who are you still in touch with from our year?' I ask one girl. She lists a few names, describing what they're up to. 'And Jess, of course. She hasn't been at all well recently, though. I just hope everything's going to be OK.'

I don't ask what's wrong. It sounds too much like cancer and if it is I can't stand here listening to her talk about it and having to go how awful, as if it were something totally alien to my own life.

The next morning, I put on the same outfit and go to Patrick and Claudia's wedding at St Etheldreda's, the Catholic church just behind Smithfield Meat Market.

Most of their close friends are here but I notice Kevin's missing. I'm surprised, as he's one of Patrick's best mates.

The music begins and Claudia, who looks like the singer Ute Lemper, walks down the aisle. The priest gives the welcome. He finishes by saying, 'Patrick and Claudia would like to dedicate this next piece of music to their friend Kevin Liddle who died on Tuesday.'

The choir soars into a Kyrie and the shock spreads across my skin.

It's just not possible. I only saw him a couple of months ago when I was round at Patrick's and Claudia's for dinner. He was fine. I was the one who was worried about dying.

'How are you?' he asked. 'Pads tells me you haven't been well.'

Lots of people ask the question, but they don't always really want to know the answer. He did, which surprised me because I didn't know him that well, and because most men don't like talking about illness.

In the distance, the mass is being sung, the readings given and the marriage ceremony takes place. All I can think is, how could this have happened?

I find out how, in the taxi, on the way to the reception.

'He took his own life,' a friend of Patrick's tells me.

'Why?'

'I think he'd been very depressed. He lost his mother to cancer in the spring. Somehow that was the last straw.'

'I had no idea he was in a bad way.'

'Often you don't. People can hide it well.'

The reception's at the Architectural Association, an architecture school on Bedford Square where Patrick teaches. I've been here loads of times, sometimes for evening lectures and a drink afterwards. And every July they have an end-of-year exhibition opening, a huge party that spills out onto the square and where you bump into just about every architect you know. I didn't go this year.

The party's in the bar, a large high-ceilinged room on the first floor with tall skinny sash windows opening onto ornamental balconies. Its architecture is almost identical to the chemotherapy room. This room, though, is filled with well-dressed, healthy-looking and mostly young people sipping champagne. Several are architects, many I know from Patrick and Claudia's parties. I'm pretty sure that Patrick, who's not known for his discretion, has told some of them I've been ill, especially when a couple of people who are normally really friendly barely acknowledge me. It's hurtful. I'm also not entirely comfortable being among so many architects, as it's a reminder of how far from that world I've travelled and that I'm no longer a hard-working successful person.

Claudia introduces me to her best friend, Ellie. She had breast cancer the year before I did. I heard about it just a couple of months before it happened to me. How awful to be dying so young, was what I thought at the time. She is tall and beautiful, with short dark curly hair. You would never guess.

Although it's the first time we've met, almost immediately we're sharing intimate details of our illness. We discover our tumours were uncannily similar; both on our left breasts, in almost exactly the same position and almost exactly the same size, mine just one millimetre bigger. I ask when she finished treatment.

'In February. Then I took another six months off. In Germany that's quite normal. It's really important to give yourself enough time to get over it and readjust.' She gives me her email in case I ever want to ask anything.

Later, Patrick's brother sways drunkenly with me on the dance floor. 'You've been so bloody brave, Bels. I know it's been really hard, but maybe something good will come out of it all.'

Patrick, equally drunk, joins us. 'So, Bels, what did you think of my mate Tom, the one I sat you next to at the meal? He's a very talented writer. You should go and seduce him.'

'He was nice, a bit intellectual. Kept talking about post-structuralism and post this and that. Anyway, Pads, I'm not really in the mood for even trying to seduce anyone right now.' And I doubt if I even could.

'You look great, though,' he slurs. The problem is, I just don't feel it.

I have my final session of radiotherapy on Monday morning. *Magic FM* plays 'Last Christmas' as the space-age arm hovers above me for the last time. A nurse shows me out and in the same breath says, 'Goodbye and good luck,' to me and calls in the next of the twenty patients on her list for the morning.

I walk over to Marylebone High Street, thinking I should be elated. It feels exactly the same as any other radiotherapy day, though.

My friend Paul's in town this week, so I've arranged to meet him for breakfast at The Providores. The last time I saw him was in New York in May, less than forty-eight hours before my operation.

He hugs me.

165

'So good to see you. I can't believe it's been over six months. How's the rest of your year been?'

'Not bad. And yours?'

'Pretty cool. Manic but exciting. Business is starting to take off and I'm still teaching at Yale once a week. I've even met someone - we got together in May. Must have been just after you left.'

We order. Green tea and brown rice and soya milk porridge for me, a latte and the Turkish eggs with chilli butter and whipped yoghurt for him. While we wait for our food, I ask about his girlfriend.

'Enough about me,' he says after I've interrogated him. 'How's that big Harrods job going?'

'It's been so much work,' I pretend. 'But it's looking great and almost done.'

'Well I hope your client's been giving you lots of free spa treatments. Whenever I think about you, I have this image of you on a massage table being pampered.'

'I wish!'

All I can think of is the other kind of treatment bed I've been lying on daily for the past six weeks.

21

I've waited months for treatment to end. The reality is, it's not as sweet as I anticipated, partly because I know in early January I'll be going back into hospital to have the other lump removed. Released from the routine of treatment, I'm also surprised to discover I almost miss the oncology unit. I've become so used to being held within its armature of doctors, nurses and others who share this illness.

Treatment gave me a structure and an objective. Now, I am unanchored and uncertain of whether I belong in the world of the sick or the well. Waiting for radiotherapy in that narrow basement corridor under the glare of the lights had become awkwardly familiar. Sitting at my computer in Jamie's black steel and concrete office in Clerkenwell now seems so alien.

I long for one hundred percent assurance that I'll never get this disease again. Instead, I'll have to live with uncertainty.

At the moment, the only illness I can think about is cancer. I know there are many other ways of getting sick or dying but I'm irrationally convinced I'm protected from every single other one. Heart attack, stroke, MS. They won't happen to me.

If I hear someone's died, I automatically assume it was from cancer, easily forgetting that every day thousands die for many other reasons.

When I hear stories about people who've had cancer, the first thing I want to know is how long they've been clear for. The time elapsed since their diagnosis is my only measure of their achievement.

Christmas is grey and secluded. The short days and long nights stretch out. I've never much liked this time of year and how in the aftermath of all the pre-Christmas excitement, London seems sad and tired. I spend most of my time at home. I've found a new addiction: crossword puzzles. I buy big books of them from the newsagents and spend hours filling in their blank boxes, seeking certainty in words. I'm not sure where else to look for it.

'Come to the sales this afternoon,' my mother suggests on the twenty-seventh. She thinks it'll do me good to get out of the house for a bit.

It's raining when we reach Oxford Street. The light's already murky, even though it's only mid-afternoon. Sleek dark pavements hold the neon glow of shop signs and traffic lights. We fight our way through canopies of umbrellas. I watch the crowds on this gloomy afternoon, laden with bags, as they stream in and out of shops festooned with large SALE banners.

Vincent, the Swede from Dubai, has texted a few times since he arrived in England to spend Christmas with his parents. We arrange to meet outside Tower Records in Piccadilly Circus the Sunday evening before New Year.

Blonde hair & brown leather jacket. How about u? he texted earlier in the day.

Brown bobbed hair & black coat.

I think back to the last email he sent me.

Can I ask you to do a small test?
1. What's the first animal that comes into your mind?
Describe how you see it.
2. What's the second animal and how do you see it?

3. Describe how you see the ocean.

4. Imagine you're walking in a beautiful forest when you come across a wall, which you can't walk round. What do you do?

I sent him my answers, telling him I wanted to know his and what this test was supposed to mean.

1. A cat. Beautiful, sleek, independent, relaxed, gets to do what it wants.

2. A bird. Can see the whole world in a way no one else can. Colourful, strange and otherworldly.

3. Vast, limitless, calming, soothing, frightening, lonely, scaleless.

4. Dissolve into light and permeate through it.

The first question is apparently how you see yourself, the second how others see you, the third how you see life and the fourth how you view death. His answers were:

1. A dog. Always happy, intelligent, full of energy.

2. A dolphin. Quick, intelligent, beautiful, smiling, lovely body

3. Beautiful, can watch it for hours, sail in it, play in it etc.

4. Climb the wall and have a look. If I liked it I'd climb over and if not, I'd turn around and go back.

Beautiful, smiling, lovely body, I repeat silently as I climb the steps out of the Tube. I glance hopefully at the people waiting outside the record shop. There's only one man in a brown leather jacket but his hair is more mouse than blonde, his body definitely average. Before I've had a chance to even think about whether to do a runner, he's walking towards me, smiling.

'Annabel?'

'Where shall we go?' he asks. 'You're a London girl so I'm sure you know some cool places.'

I suggest Wardour Street.

In the bar at Mezzo, he asks what I want to drink.

'A fruit juice, please.'

'Are you sure you don't want something alcoholic?'

I start telling him about my post-Christmas detox, elaborating on how I went to too many drunken parties in December and how, apart from New Year's Eve of course, I've given up alcohol for at least a month.

He talks at length about the mobile phone industry and beach life in Dubai. When he asks to see my phone, he's unimpressed to discover it's a large old Nokia.

'Ericsson's much better - I'm not just saying it as I work for them. It's so cool, I get the newest models before they're on the market.'

'That's nice.' I try and feign interest.

'Shall we get something to eat?' he asks an hour later.

I'm tempted to tell him I'm really tired and have to go home, but as he's come from Surrey and it's only just gone eight, it seems a bit mean. At least food might help fill the conversational gaps, which are starting to expand.

I suggest Busaba, the Thai restaurant a few doors down. It's always crowded and noisy and should drown out any silences.

'This is delicious.' He rolls Phad Thai noodles round his fork, having confessed to an inability with chopsticks. 'It's nice to be out with a proper London girl.'

When he goes to the loo, I check my mobile. There's a new text.

Happy Christmas and all the best for 2003, Andreas.

I haven't heard from him in over two months and it's obvious it's a general message. I've forced myself to forget him, but even just receiving this makes me smile.

Vincent comes back and starts telling me about the toilets. 'They've got the same basin for men and women - there's a gap between the bottom of the mirror and the basin so you can actually see people washing their hands on the other side. I've never seen anything like it.'

'I know. I've been here loads of times.'

I want to go home after dinner but he suggests another drink. In a pub on Brewer Street, I count the minutes as I watch Vincent drink a pint of Guinness. Outside Piccadilly Circus Tube, we kiss each other on the cheeks and promise to stay in touch even though I know we won't.

I spend New Year's Eve at a Greek restaurant in Primrose Hill with Tanya, Axel and a few of their friends. We leave just before midnight and walk up to the top of the hill. The year turns and a part of me wants to cry with relief that 2002 is finally over. Yet this shift in digits seems so artificial. Can you really draw a line under things just because the date changes?

London is spread out below us. A latticework of lights thread themselves across the city's surface. They trace the outlines of tower blocks, cranes, monuments, extending for miles before peeling away into darkness. The sky flares with the colour and noise of fireworks.

I look across this vast city. My story is just one of many millions being played out. Where will it lead me?

22

In early January, I go back to hospital. Before I check in, I'm told to go to the surgeon's offices round the corner to have an ultrasound so they can scan me and locate and mark up this secret lump buried inside my breast.

I know I'll be made to take my wig off for surgery so instead of the awkwardness of being seen with two different looks and having everyone know I'm wearing one, I decide it's easier to leave it at home.

Each week I measure my hair with the tape measure I once used for checking dimensions on site. It's now thirty-two millimetres long. There were also a few longer strands left over from before, but I've hacked them off with a pair of nail scissors so it's now all sort of the same length.

Hair this short is not a look I'd have ever chosen. Although I was always curious how it might be on me. It's interesting how by simply changing your hair length you can look so different. In my case, edgier, with larger eyes.

I walk down Harley Street, my head hidden under a hat. My scan's done by the same doctor as last May and November. I'm self-conscious, as he's the first person apart from my mother who's seen my wigless head, but he doesn't say anything. I guess he's used to it.

He glides the probe across my skin and I'm anxious that, in the two months since I was last scanned, something could have changed.

'It's still exactly the same size and definitely looks benign,' he reassures me. I don't remind him that last May he used almost exactly the same words.

In my head, I swing between two different stories. One is that the lump hasn't grown in eight months and as far as I know cancerous tumours tend to grow quite quickly. After the misfortune of having had cancer, I'm now due some good luck, so I'm sure it'll all be fine.

The other story replays the surgeon's words from last November: *incredibly rare, but it has been known for a cancerous tumour to hide behind a benign one.* It's the one where I tell myself that if my body created a cancer once, then why not again? And my doctors have been wrong before.

Statistically, it would be very, very unlikely to have two separate breast cancers diagnosed within eight months and for the doctors to get it wrong twice, my optimistic head retorts back. But the other side reminds it that some people are just really unlucky. Images of chemotherapy float, unwanted, into my mind. Stop it, I tell myself. We'll deal with that if and when we need to.

When I come out of the surgeon's offices, it's started to snow. Reassuring and protective, the flakes drift down, blanketing and quietening everything. I walk along Marylebone High Street towards the hospital, enjoying the sensation of snowflakes dissolving on my face. I go into the newsagents and buy yet another book of bumper crosswords and browse through the magazines. Most of the January issues have headlines like *New Year, New You,* or *Detox Yourself in 2 Weeks.* They make it sound so easy.

In the hospital, I share the lift up to my room with a guy about my age, who tells me he's in for a knee operation. He smiles at me. 'This is just like being in a hotel.' Once I thought that, too.

The anaesthetist comes into my room. He doesn't comment on my hair.

'Hello, it's you again. Just can't seem to stay away,' he teases.

I remember how the first time I was here he told me I had to stay positive, passing on the story of his famous pianist patient who was playing better than ever since she had breast cancer. Back then, his words seemed ridiculous. Now it's one of a small collection of stories I've heard, which include the one about the Australian nurse's grandmother who got it at my age and died at ninety-three. Recently, I read a book by a woman who was diagnosed with ovarian cancer at twenty-three and given two months to live. She completely changed her lifestyle and has been cancer free for over twenty years. I often return to these stories, especially on days like this.

I lie on the trolley in the basement, waiting for the anaesthetist to give me the injection. I can't stop shaking. Even I hadn't realised how scared I actually am.

The veins on my right arm are still bruised and raw from chemotherapy and pain sears through me as twice he fails to insert the needle.

'We're not doing too well here. You've got tiny veins and most of the ones on this side have already blown.'

'Can't you just put it in my left arm?'

'You've had lymph nodes removed so we're not allowed to.'

'Even if I let you?'

He shakes his head, now stabbing at my right hand. 'The veins here seem a bit better, though I'm afraid it's going to be even more painful than through the arm. In a few seconds you'll be asleep, though.'

I shut my eyes and keep my scream silent as he plunges the needle in.

I spend the afternoon waiting. Waiting for the nausea to pass, waiting anxiously for some news. My mother sits with me for a while and my sister comes by when she's finished teaching. My father is in Russia for work.

In the late afternoon, when I'm alone again, the anaesthetist comes back.

'Now, I'm not supposed to say this, as he always likes to break the news himself. But I'm delighted to tell you that everything looked absolutely fine. Just don't let on you already know.'

As soon as he shuts the door, I start crying. With relief, because it's all fine, but also with sadness, because this is exactly what the doctors should have said to me last time. Then, it didn't really cross my mind they'd say anything else. But today it feels hard-earned and it makes me sad to realise how much my expectations have changed.

I look out of the window. It's so different to that late afternoon last May when I lay in a different room in the same building. Today, the sky's already darkening and the snow's still falling. This wintry landscape feels comforting. It may sound silly, but even though I was scared this morning, at some deeper level, which I couldn't even voice to myself, as soon as I saw the snow, I knew everything would be alright.

The surgeon comes in an hour later, his scrubs replaced by a smart double-breasted suit.

'Very good news indeed. Nothing suspicious at all, just a fibroadenoma. I'll have the official pathology back on Monday so I'll see you at my offices then.'

I beam at him, pretending to be surprised.

In the evening, I get visits from Anat, Paola and Ioana. The first thing they all tell me is how much they like my hair short.

'It's brilliant,' says Ioana. 'You've got the right shaped face. It really shows up your bone structure. Just get a little trim done and stop wearing your wig. I'm sure guys will love it.'

I can't sleep. I'm too excited, elated by how well everything went today. I spend most of the night awake, doing crossword after crossword.

When I open the curtains the next morning, it's still snowing. The grey pavements and brown brick buildings opposite are masked in white. I sit in the armchair by the window, mesmerised by the tumbling crystals.

I'm discharged just after ten. My mother collects me. Muffled under snow, the city feels slower, muted. We drive along the edge of Regent's Park. Today its interior is shrouded from the street by the thick snow clinging to its hedges and railings. When she drove me back from hospital last time, I remember thinking how the park's spring pleasure garden was a suddenly a world to which I no longer belonged.

'You should get some rest,' my mother says when we get home.

'I'm too hyped-up to sleep.'

The following day, I come crashing down. Outside, the snow's already dissolving into slush, exposing the grimy tones of this January day. No one calls. My friends are back at work and I am no longer officially ill. I wander listlessly around the house not quite knowing what to do with myself or what happens next.

At the surgeon's office, a nurse leads me into the small side room with the mirror window and drawers of medical instruments. She tells me to remove everything above the waist.

He comes in, strips off the small piece of white gauze taped to my breast and examines his work. In the mirror I see the one-inch red line scored across the underside of my right breast. I'm relieved to see it's so much smaller than the scar on the other side and its location means it won't ever spill out from the edges of any clothing.

In his consulting room, he picks up a piece of paper from the mahogany desk.

'"A nine-millimetre benign fibroadenoma with no atypical features." And I'm pleased to see you looking so well. A lot of people come out of all of this very pale and thin.'

'I did lose lots of weight during chemo. It was one of the few advantages.'

'That's a terrible thing to think.' He's only half chuckling. 'Now come and see me again in May. In the meantime, you can get on with the rest of your life.'

At reception, on my way out, I notice one of those desktop calendars, which have a different page for each day of the year. *Monday January 13th 2003*, it reads. I remember another Monday the thirteenth, a May day, exactly eight months ago. That day I crossed over into a different world. Today, am I crossing back over again?

23

I have images, perhaps I should call them fantasies, of what my life might be like:

Soon, I should be over the exhaustion. I'll take it easy for a while and enjoy myself. I'll do yoga every day, lose the weight I've put on in the last few months, see lots of exhibitions, go out with my friends, relax in cafes with a book. Perhaps I'll take a holiday. Within a couple of months I'll be feeling fantastic. By then I'll also know exactly what I want to do with the rest of my life and will just go for it. And hopefully soon I'll meet someone wonderful, too.

Weeks later, I'm still completely exhausted. Every morning I wake up feeling no better than the one before. Each day drags by as if I were walking through mud. I'm surprised to find myself quite depressed and lacking much enthusiasm or purpose. It doesn't make any sense. I ought to be happy about having finished treatment and hopefully being clear of this disease.

While I want to grab life with both hands, it's also a scary prospect as the more you have, the more you risk losing. In some ways, it's easier to remain mentally in the illness world. There, you have fewer expectations.

Once, I longed simply to live. Viewed from the darkness of illness, the ordinary world seemed remarkable. But now, as I try to move back towards it, all I can think about is how much I've lost.

This time last year, I remember rushing between work, my social life, yoga, the gym. I'd sometimes go to lectures after work - fashionable Swiss and Dutch architects like Herzog de Meuron and MVDV. There were nights out in Hoxton Square, a friend's film screening in Golden Square, another friend's band played in Islington. I saw exhibitions - Mario Testino at the National, Nan Goldin at the Whitechapel.

Now, my diary's almost empty.

I'm convalescing, I try and tell myself. It's OK not to have much going on for a while. I still see my close friends, although I'm out of touch with my more casual ones. We go for quiet dinners at places like Manna and I always try and be home by ten.

While I was having treatment, I was surrounded by others with cancer, many of whom were probably a lot sicker than I was. Then, I often felt grateful to be, within that world, one of the luckier ones. As Dr Jones once said to me, 'Often I have to sit at this table and tell someone the best odds I can give are fifty-fifty. Yours are quite a bit better.'

But now, when I look at my friends, none of whom have had cancer and who've instead spent the past year getting on with their careers and relationships - things you're supposed to focus on in your early thirties - I'm angry. Before, I sometimes managed to be more philosophical. On occasion I'd even think, why not me? After all, I had experienced no major traumas during the first thirty years of my life. I also hoped that the silver lining to this experience would be that I'd be left with a more heightened appreciation of life.

Now, I'm disappointed to discover the reality is quite different.

Almost everyone else assumes now treatment's over that's it. As if it can end as suddenly as it all began:

179

You're OK now, aren't you?

You're looking really well.

What are you doing these days now it's all over?

I wish it were that simple, but I inhabit a body and a mind that tell me otherwise. I know people just want to be reassured that I am well again. And I'm sure it also makes them more comfortable no longer to have to dwell upon the dark spaces of illness and suffering.

I also know I can be difficult to please. When people assume I'm fine, I get annoyed because they don't understand what it's really like. But when anyone commiserates with me over how terrible it must have been, I'm also annoyed because I don't want to be pitied.

I want to be asked how I am actually feeling and not to be told, 'I'm glad everything's going so *well*,' as I am by a close family friend, one of the few I let my mother tell.

Everything's not going so fucking well, actually, I want to say. I feel like shit and now I have to live with the worry that this could come back. But I'm way too polite to do that, especially as I know he's only trying to be nice.

But I wish people would listen to what I have to say, even if it isn't what they might want to hear. It's not that I want to drone on about how miserable I am all the time, but I don't want the truth to have to be a closed territory either.

In mid-January I go back to my job teaching architecture every Thursday at Kingston University. I've been there almost four years, assisting Patrick with his group of students.

I'm nervous about going back. I haven't worked in nine months and it's very much a thinking-on-your-feet kind of job where students bring in their design projects and you're supposed to help them resolve any problems and inspire them to move forward. These days, I feel like such a non-architect. I used to go to all those lectures, read the magazines, buy the books. The last one I bought was over a year ago, on Peter Zumthor, whose thermal baths in Switzerland I visited just a month before I found the lump. For almost a year, I've read only novels and alternative health books. I've also missed the first term of the project, for artists' workshops and housing on a site in Florence, which everyone else visited with Patrick in the autumn.

Do the students and other tutors know why I suddenly disappeared last year? Chances are that Patrick, who doesn't hold back on much, has told them. But apart from one other tutor, a very over the top Greek woman, no one mentions it.

'You must be brave, you must be brave.' She kisses me profusely when I run into her in the corridor. Her show is disconcerting. Does she think I need to be brave because it's going to come back? Others, thankfully, only comment on my *great new haircut*.

As usual, the tutors go to the local pub for lunch. When we walk in, the stale grease smell hits me. I never noticed it before, but since chemo my sense of smell's much more sensitive. I used to almost always have fish and chips, but today I'm not sure what to order. Everything's fried or has meat or cheese in it. I ask for a salad sandwich.

The others talk shop, discussing their students, the new head of school who arrived in September and I've never met, and their own architecture practices. I used to be at ease in this setting. Today, I am very quiet and, even though it's only lunchtime, very tired. I'm slouched in my seat, arms wrapped round me, black coat still on. Am I trying to make myself invisible?

'What are you up to at the moment?' a couple of people ask.

'Still at Jamie's, working on the Harrods spa,' I fib.

'How's that coming along?'

Luckily, I spoke to Jamie last week.

'Almost finished, late of course, but most of the phases are now open. There are a couple left to snag and just the café's still on site.'

In the evening, I take the train back to Waterloo with Patrick. He chats away about his career plans. 'I'm thinking of applying for a teaching post at Cambridge next year. I'm quite keen to try the States, too. They take academics seriously over there and pay them properly. I don't know if I could convince Claudia, though.'

As I listen to him, a part of me wishes I were also working hard, achieving things and able to sound impressive. The driven, ambitious side of me feels guilty for doing so little at the moment. I have to remind myself that my experience of life these past months has been so different to his. It's inevitable that we won't be in the same place.

I'm still having therapy. Surprised by how hard I'm finding things, it's a relief to be able to talk to Javier.

'So, what exactly do you think you've lost?' he asks one day.

'Before I got ill, apart from not having a boyfriend everything in my life was fine. Now I'm having to start over again. I'm thirty-two and living with my parents. I don't have a job and I'm not sure what I'm going to do with my life. I know it's really trivial but I feel fat and it'll be ages until my hair's long again. I've also lost my trust in the world. I used to think maybe I'd be lucky and nothing really terrible would happen to me. Very naïve, of course. Now I'm scared loads of other bad things could happen, too.'

'It's a transition period,' he says in his heavy Spanish accent with the flawless English. 'Oddly, it's often the way - you're more depressed after a serious illness than in the middle of it.'

'Surely now's when I should be happy again?'

'Surprisingly not.' He explains how during these past months I was probably so caught up in the shock of the diagnosis and getting myself through the treatment that I'd have just dealt with things on a day-to-day basis. It's only in the aftermath that I can look back and comprehend what's happened and the impact it's had on my life.

'It's really important to allow yourself time to fully recover. I'm sure people are telling you to just put it behind you and move on. But usually the body knows what we need. I think it'd help you to listen to it and not try to fight it or feel guilty about the exhaustion and sadness.'

I am reminded of what the breast care nurse at the oncology unit said to me last summer: *this illness will take eighteen months out of your life.*

At the time, I couldn't believe it would be that long and I ignored her words. Now, I realise she may have been right. It's frustrating. I want to get on with things and start enjoying my life again, especially since I can no longer assume it'll last eighty or ninety years.

'Am I going to feel like this forever?' When you're stuck in something, it can be hard to believe things will ever change.

'Definitely not. It just may take more time than you'd like.'

'You hear people in magazine articles saying stuff like cancer's the best thing that's ever happened to them. That it's made them appreciate their lives even more. I wanted it to be like that.'

He raises his thick eyebrows slightly as I tell him that I'd hoped the scales would balance out and because I'd been through something bad, good things would come to me in return.

'Life isn't fair. The world doesn't owe you anything because of this. Once you're fully recovered, the difference may be how you feel inside. That's what could change your life.'

'What do you mean?'

'How you feel inside has a big impact on how you experience life. Putting aside what's going on right now, which seems quite normal, the fact that you've been through this illness and the particular way you've handled it - by trying to understand yourself better - means that your life may well change. But it won't happen overnight and it won't be because someone up there feels sorry for you.'

It's ridiculous how uncomfortable I am with the way my body has changed. I survive cancer, yet I'm worrying about having short hair instead of long, going from a pre-cancer size ten to an un-toned twelve, and a couple of scars.

I argue back and forth with myself.

Don't be so shallow. At least you have a body and it's in one piece. What if you'd lost your legs?

But I'm a young single woman. I want to be attractive.

In other people's eyes, you probably still are. Lots of men love short hair and you aren't fat, really.

I don't feel good like this.

Perhaps try and change your rigid view of what makes a person attractive?

I stop feeling quite so sorry for myself the day I come across a severely disabled man trying to get on the bus in the pouring rain as I'm on my way to teach at Kingston. While I'm sitting comfortably in my seat, he's on the pavement in his wheelchair wailing furious and incoherent fragments of words. When he's finally on the bus, he stops his wheelchair right in front of my seat and a couple of times during the journey swings his body round to face me, arms flailing, spit flying out of his mouth, rage in his eyes. Whenever I catch myself complaining about how I can't get into my old jeans, I remind myself of him.

I discover the Breast Cancer Care website. There's a section called Chat containing several online forums. The Younger

Women one jumps out. With a huge sense of relief, I finally find myself in a space filled with people like me. It's the first time I've been in a chat room. I stay for hours, reading through page after page of threads. Where to get good wigs, how chemo affects your sex drive, and whether to go dairy free are just a few of the topics covered. It's like coming home after months wandering in the desert.

Even though we, classified as those under forty, are a tiny percentage of the statistics, we number many. I thought thirty-one was young to get it, but some women are in their twenties.

I start visiting the site several times a day, hungrily checking for new posts. Some names I see again and again, and many of them seem to have, at least virtually, become quite close to each other. In this world, I feel quite lucky. A lovely sounding twenty-three-year-old called Gemma, who got married last year, has secondary bone cancer. Another woman's husband left her during treatment. What's also interesting is how so many people have been treated badly by those who knew they were ill. Friends who stopped calling, or people who proceeded to tell them about everyone they knew who died of cancer. It makes me glad I was selective about who I told.

My mother gets cross with me for constantly clogging up her phone line. When I explain how it helps makes me feel less isolated she says, 'OK, but no more than twenty minutes at a time.' Whenever she goes out, I'm usually straight back on there.

At first, I'm just a voyeur. Then, I tentatively post a message.
Has anyone else felt rubbish after treatment was over?
The responses come quickly. Again and again I'm told by women I don't know how they felt exactly the same. One, who admittedly was depressed for years before, even took an overdose. At least I don't feel quite that bad.

In this space, normal values are overturned

I'm cracking open the champagne tonight, Mandy writes. She's just had her results back. *A fast growing four-centimetre tumour.* Try getting anyone outside this world to raise their glass to that. But she's celebrating as the tumour hasn't spread to her lymph nodes.

At first, I refuse to click on the forum entitled Secondary Breast Cancer. But seeing it listed there day after day, morbid curiosity soon lures me in. Many of the threads have depressing titles like Lara G Now at Peace, Brain Mets, or End of the Road. The worst stories are those where a tumour, initially similar to mine, has come back.

I have to remind myself that there are probably thousands of other women who've had breast cancer and are absolutely fine. They just won't be found hanging out on a secondaries website.

What surprises me is how some describe happiness, in spite of terminal cancer.

One woman writes that as she knows she might die soon, she's stripped her life right back and is just focusing on what really matters - the people she loves. She just wishes she'd found out earlier how unimportant most of the stuff she used to worry about was.

Don't you feel cheated, knowing it's all going to be taken away soon, I want to ask. She is only forty-seven.

Meanwhile, I still have the luxury of being irritated when I miss my train to Kingston or get stuck in the wrong queue at the supermarket checkout.

24

In Regent's Park occasional crocus and daffodil buds are breaking tentatively through the ground; fragile whispers of purple and yellow against the black soil.

London is hit by Valentine fever. The shops are filled with hearts - pink satin, cardboard, fur, chocolate. Right now, the possibility of love feels remote. In my mind I want it, but I'm not sure I'm ready. Love means being prepared to invest and to risk losing a lot. I'm still reeling from the losses of the past year.

It seems right to be insular at the moment. I like thinking of myself as a butterfly, waiting to emerge from its cocoon.

I've recently started trying to put this experience into words. I've always wanted to write something, I was just never quite sure what. A few months ago, I realised I had my subject matter.

When I was diagnosed, I couldn't find anything about going through breast cancer when you're young, single, and childless. Ruth Picardie's brilliant *Before I Say Goodbye*, which I happened to read the year before I was diagnosed, is the story of a thirty-two-year-old married woman with young children, whose breast cancer was already quite advanced when diagnosed. Right after my own diagnosis, I stupidly re-read it, terrifying myself. But that was the only story I could even find about a young woman.

I'm sitting at the computer for a couple of hours every day. The words just pour out, in a totally random and unstructured way - fragments of thoughts, feelings and events. I have no idea how to make them into a story.

Ioana calls just before Valentine's Day.

'Chris and I broke up.'

I'm surprised. I assumed they'd stay together at least a few months.

'Anyway, I wanted to tell you there's a Valentine's singles party on Friday in some new bar on Holloway Road. My friend Carlos sent an email. Kwong's coming.'

Ioana, Kwong and I sit on a bench at the back of the bar trying to talk above the music. It bounces off the black painted walls and I can feel it pound inside me. No one's really dancing.

'Do you know many people?' I ask Ioana.

'Not really - just Carlos and a couple of the girls look familiar. I've probably seen them at parties before.'

It's a South American crowd, and the women are beautiful. I can't believe they are all single. 'All too fussy,' my mother would say.

'Going to chat anyone up?' I tease Kwong.

'That one at the bar with dark hair and the backless top looks cool.'

'Go and talk to her,' suggests Ioana.

'Maybe later. Hey, it's just like the old days - the three of us out together - we haven't done this in ages.'

The last time we did it was the night I found the lump, but I don't mention this as Kwong doesn't even know I've been ill.

We stay just over an hour and don't make the effort to talk to anyone else. I'm glad they're not feeling especially sociable either. It's been ages since I've been to a party, yet alone one where I know virtually no one. I'm not a natural extrovert and my ability to chat or flirt with strangers is like a muscle which, unless I regularly use it, loses its tone. Tonight, most of my words would probably have stayed trapped inside.

I was planning to carry on wearing the wig until my hair was longer. On the Tube one day, I pick up a copy of *Metro* and find an article about how several top London salons are offering free haircuts to women who've recently been through chemotherapy. The Aveda salon in Covent Garden, which I was project architect for, is on the list. Much as I'd always wanted a haircut there, I decide to go somewhere where I can be completely anonymous. I call the number at the end of the article to ask if there's anywhere they particularly recommend.

A friendly American voice answers the phone. 'I've had breast cancer too,' she says, 'and I've been going to a place in Holborn called Brookes and Brookes. See Sally. She's one of the owners and she's brilliant.'

The only appointment available is on a Thursday evening. I go straight there from my teaching day at Kingston. I've been wearing my wig and don't want to have to go into the salon and take it off in front of strangers so I stand on the corner of Southampton Row and High Holborn, my back towards the rush hour traffic, quickly remove it and put it in my bag, hoping no-one noticed. I run my fingers through my hair, crushed against the wig all day. What shocks me is how cold, without the wig's insulation, my head is this February night.

It's the first time I've been to the hairdresser since last July. This place has oak floors and white walls and counters. Tasteful but safe. Very different to Aveda.

'I want it a bit raw,' George, our client, told us. He got excited about the cast concrete walls, polished screed floors and black steel counters we designed. Jack of Billericay, who put in the cheapest tender, was duly appointed to build it. More than once,

I'd arrive on site to find the place reeking of dope and Jack and his team happily chilling on the floor, tools down.

An open-faced woman about my age introduces herself as Sally. Her accent is northern. 'So, what are we doing today?'

'I'm here on the *Metro* offer. I finished chemotherapy a few months ago and my hair's a mess. It's never been cut. Is it long enough for you to tidy up?'

'Of course. I've shaped hair shorter than this before. Yours seems to be growing back really fast.'

In the chair next to me, a tanned woman is having foils put in her long blonde hair and telling her hairdresser she just got back from Carnival in Rio.

'Some women I see who've been through the same thing can't carry short hair very well. You're lucky, you've got the right shaped face,' Sally says as she clips away. 'One of my clients, about your age, had hers come back grey afterwards. This is a lovely dark brown. Was it the same before?'

'It was brown but I can't remember exactly what shade. I'd been dyeing it for ages.'

'What are you planning next?'

'The natural look. All that colour really damaged it. It's possibly one of the reasons it fell out so easily.'

'Did you have the curls before, too?'

'Yes. They drove me nuts. I always wanted straight hair. I'd hoped it might come back like that. Apparently, you sometimes you get the opposite of what you had. To be honest, I'm just so glad to have hair back that I don't even care whether it's brown and curly. I can't wait for it to be long again.'

I tell her I've even thought about having extensions put in. 'We don't do them here,' she says. 'I've heard there's a good place in Chalk Farm where Posh and Co. go. But I think you should just enjoy this look, though. Before you know it, it'll be long again.'

Back at home, I stare at myself in the mirror for ages, trying to decide what I think of it. My hair's always swung between bobbed and shoulder length. I can't say this short doesn't suit me but I don't feel like myself. I've heard so many times how women who lost their hair through chemo ended up keeping it short, as they actually preferred it that way. I know I won't be one of them.

I take out my tape measure. My hair's now forty-seven millimetres. I hold the tape from the crown of my head to my shoulders. Three hundred and seventy millimetres. Hair grows approximately half an inch a month so I calculate it will take twenty-five months to reach my shoulders. I'll also lose some length each time it's trimmed, so it'll probably be around two and a half years.

It's actually a relief to shed the wig. I no longer have to worry about people touching my head, or that it could fall off in an upside-down yoga position. Almost everyone likes it short. One friend thinks it's the best haircut I've ever had. Someone else goes, 'You know, they say a woman who cuts all her hair off is about to change her whole life.'

What she doesn't know is how much my life has already changed.

25

'Shall we go skiing for a long weekend?' my friend Julieann asks.

Last March, two months before I was diagnosed, we skied together in Switzerland. We've taken a few trips over the years, including Interrailing at the end of our first year of university and six weeks backpacking round Central America at the end of our second. When we went skiing, she managed to slide halfway down a black slope before she even got her skis on. We spent the rest of the day in floods of laughter.

'I'd love to,' I tell her. 'But I'm still pretty knackered so I'm not sure how much fun I'll be.'

'Doesn't matter. It'll just be nice to have a break. Let's try that place you like in the Dolomites.'

I was supposed to go there last summer with my family but had to cancel because of chemotherapy. At the time, I worried I might never return.

We fly to Italy on a beautiful early March day. Passing over the snow encrusted Alps, it surprises me how much of the area seems completely uninhabited. There are no villages or roads, even in the valleys. For how many centuries have these mountains stood here?

I've always found being in the mountains, especially in winter, comforting. They have a quality of timelessness. I love the cold clean air, the warm pine-scented interiors and the simple food.

Julieann and I stand together at the top of the chair lift the next morning, skis on our feet. The light, bouncing off the snow, is so much brighter than in London. There, all the grey and brown surfaces seem to swallow it up.

'I'm so glad to be here,' I tell her.

As usual, for the first few minutes it's strange having these long narrow things attached to my feet. Moving and turning on them seems alien. But soon my body remembers what to do and loses itself in the rhythm of travelling across the landscape. I skim across the snow-covered contours, a cool breeze across my face, my blood warm, and I'm exhilarated. Right now, nothing else seems to really matter.

'Are you tired?' Julieann asks when we stop for lunch.

'Not at all. It's strange but since we got here, it's the first time I feel completely normal again. Almost as if everything that happened was just a bad dream.'

I'm even skiing faster than usual. I used to be quite scared of falling. But now I'm thinking how there's no point being scared of something which either might not happen, or if it does, would have done so regardless. I wish I could take this approach to everything.

I think a part of me is also curious to experience some physical discomfort that has nothing to do with cancer. What I hate about cancer is its silence and painlessness. It's creepy as it can trick you into thinking you're OK while all along it's in there, furtively wreaking havoc. So, in a weird way it'd be a relief to experience the honesty of pain that actually mirrors the damage caused. But incredibly, I get through the whole trip without a single fall.

We've only been away four days but when we return London has changed, in that way it suddenly can. It's almost spring. Some of the branches are still bare but many are now full with blossom, like lace canopies. Spring has always been my favourite season, particularly its early days when the air softens and everything starts to grow again, while in the coolness and early sunsets, the memory of winter still hovers.

There's a lilac bush outside my parents' house and at night you can now smell it again. It's a scent I have always associated with this time of year, reminding me of all the ones gone by, and for the first time making me hope, rather than assume, that there will be many more.

Since we got back my mood's different. I'm less tired and the darkness is slowly lifting. It's not an entirely smooth process; more like walking through a mountainous landscape where a steep and rocky terrain suddenly flattens out to an easy meadow and you think there's nothing left to climb. But then you turn a corner and, unexpectedly, it's steep again.

'It's normal for it not to be linear but come in waves,' Javier reassures me. 'Gradually the bad days will become less frequent, though.'

There are times I actually feel happy again. I notice it during a late afternoon walk in Regent's Park. The light is starting to go. Three swans sit by the lake, S-bending their necks in unison and crying out into the silence. The windows in the cream Nash terraces around the park glow a warm yellow. Wrapped in my coat, I have a sense of serenity and completeness, a feeling that at this moment, everything is just as it should be.

In early April, I return to the oncology unit for a check-up with Dr Jones. It'll be the first time I've been there since December.

While I was having treatment I almost never had dreams about cancer, but since it's over I've had quite a few. The night before my appointment I dream I'm having chemotherapy again. I'm sent into the toilets to give a urine sample. The cubicles are all unisex with only waist-high partitions between them. They are all occupied by naked, skeletal men and women without hair.

I walk down Harley Street feeling slightly sick. The closer I get to number eighty-one, the more nervous I become. I hesitate at the bottom of the stone steps. The spiral shapes at the top of the black metal gate-posts as usual look menacing. To me, they've always announced this as a building where unpleasant things happen. I wish they'd cut them off. They're probably listed, though.

As soon as I've walked through the front door and am standing on the familiar black and white diamond patterned floor, it's as if I've never been away. The red-haired Irish receptionist is sitting behind the mahogany desk at the end of the hallway. 'Good to see you again,' she says. 'And looking so well, too.'

I've made an extra effort with my appearance today, putting on makeup and my beige leather jacket. I want to look well, to create as much distance as possible between me and cancer.

On my way up to the second floor waiting room, I pass by the entrance to the chemotherapy room. They usually keep the tall double doors closed, but today they're open. I don't let myself look inside as I know it'll only make me retch.

There are two couples in the waiting room. I take a seat next to the older pair, who look about the same age as my parents. Across the room are a much younger couple. She has a bloated face, short hair and a piece of blood-stained gauze wrapped round her wrist. I feel so removed from and yet so close to her situation, like we're at points on a circle that are at both three hundred and sixty and zero degrees apart.

Most people seem to bring someone to their appointments. I always come alone. Having my mother or sister there would

195

actually make me more anxious as I'd be picking up on their worry, too. And I like being able to ask the doctors what I want without having to think about anyone else's reactions to my questions.

The older man next to me is trying to read *The Telegraph*. His wife constantly interrupts. 'I'm telling you, you've got to take an afternoon nap every day while you're having all this chemotherapy.'

'I'd rather take the dogs out for a walk,' he replies, irritated.

Their daughter, who's about my age, arrives, and I pretend to read a magazine while listening to their conversation.

'You're late,' the wife snaps.

'Darling, let me take your coat and get you some coffee,' says her father, quickly standing up.

'I can do it myself,' she says, quite aggressively and sits down as far from her parents as possible.

I'm curious about how cancer affects a family's relationship. Were these two women as ratty before he got ill? You'd think it would bring people closer together, but I can imagine it's probably also easy to feel angry with someone for being ill; angry because you might lose them, and also because of how it shakes up your life, too.

I don't really like thinking about how it's been for my family. It makes me feel guilty that, albeit inadvertently, I've caused them a lot of pain. To be honest, I'm glad it's been this way round as it'd be even worse to have watched one of them go through it. When you're in it you're in it and, scary and uncomfortable as it is, you just have to get on with it. When it's someone you love, I imagine it could breed even more anxiety as you're constantly watching them, worrying about what's really going on inside.

My family have been incredibly supportive. Spending so much time together has made us even closer. Apart from the big row with my mother last summer, they've let me get on with doing what I want. I thought my parents might be sceptical of things like healing and vitamin injections, but if they are, they've kept it to themselves. And while my dad's not exactly the opinionated type, my mother's not known for holding back.

I pick up a newspaper from the coffee table. On the front cover, there's a picture of a boy with no arms. It describes how Ali Abbas, a twelve-year-old boy, was orphaned and severely injured in the recent Baghdad bombings. It's a level of pain I can't even begin to imagine.

Dr Jones, wearing a fitted lime green sweater and black trousers, calls me in.

'You're looking wonderful. Love the hair. It really suits you short - sort of French and very elegant. Now, how are you?'

It's a question I'm slightly uncomfortable answering, especially when a doctor asks. I want to say I'm well, thanks, but something inside holds me back. What if that were playing with fate and she were to tell me that I'm actually not well?

Instead I settle for the more neutral, 'I'm ok, thanks.'

'Good. Let me have a quick check.'

I lie down on the bed. She circles her fingers round my breasts and digs them into my armpits, then moves them over my liver and across my abdomen. I know she's checking for secondaries, any sign of enlargement of my liver or other organs that would give cause for concern. When her hands pause briefly, I stiffen. What's she found?

'All seems fine,' she reassures me. 'I'm just being very thorough.' Then she gets me to sit up and taps her fingers down my spine before saying, 'As far as I can see, you're in perfect health.'

Perfect health, makes me smile. Even though it was preceded by the more cautious, *As far as I can see,* and I know that things can suddenly change. It's the first time since this happened, that anyone's used those words to describe me. It suggests the possibility that maybe things can go back to where they were.

I get dressed and sit back down at the desk.

'I still find it hard not to worry whenever something doesn't feel quite right.'

'That's normal. You've had a huge shock, at an age when you don't expect something like this to happen. You probably never had any reason not to trust your body before and then it suddenly goes and dramatically lets you down.'

'But does the fear ever completely go away?'

'It'll probably never go away completely but it tends to fade so much you almost forget it. It's a bit like throwing a pebble into water and watching the ripples spread further and further apart. Just call if anything's worrying you. That's what I'm here for.'

'There's one other thing I wanted to ask. Since finishing chemo I've put on quite a bit of weight.' I'm aware that it might sound rather trivial. Especially when I still have two arms and two breasts. 'I'm finding it hard to shift. Is that common?'

'It does seem to happen quite a bit. I think it's a combination of being exhausted and that the drugs may have also slowed your metabolism down temporarily. I did think you got too thin last summer, though.'

I thought I looked great.

'That's a lovely jacket by the way,' she says as I stand up to leave. 'Joseph?'

'No, Zara.'

'Well, it looks very chic.'

It's Good Friday, that time of year where so many dates are now loaded with significance. Today is April the eighteenth. Exactly a year ago I went to see the doctor about the lump for the first time. I remember being so busy at work and thinking how annoying it was that he couldn't give me an appointment before nine-thirty.

This afternoon, I go to Bach's *St Matthew* Passion at St George's Church on Hanover Square with my parents and Tanya and Axel. We were here last Good Friday. During the performance, I had this sudden vision of my funeral taking place in the church. A week later I found the lump. For a long time, I was convinced I'd had some sort of weird premonition.

The Passion is one of my favourite pieces of music. It always moves me but usually it's only right at the end as Jesus is put to his grave and the choir sings, *Lie thou softly, softly here, Rest thy worn and bruised body,* that the tears might come.

Today, as soon as the music fills the church a shock wave of emotion spreads through my whole body and across my skin. I want to sob my eyes out. It's from a mixture of sadness over what I've been through, and the joy and relief of still being here. I don't want anyone else to see how emotional I am so instead I pinch my thigh to stem the tears, and focus on the blues, purples and yellows of the stained-glass window behind the altar.

On the Tuesday after Easter, I go shopping on Oxford Street. Since I put on weight on last autumn, I've hardly been into clothes shops. But in the last few weeks I've been a bit more active and have managed to lose a few pounds. I've still got a few more to go until I'm back to my pre-cancer weight.

Top Shop's packed with teenagers on school holidays. I manage to just about squeeze myself into a pair of size ten hipsters. It feels like a small victory, even though I don't actually like them. Around the corner, Liberty has a spring sale on. I try on a pair of Juicy Couture flared jeans in my old size. I have to tug the fabric hard to get the button to close but choose not to get the bigger ones as these will be a good incentive to lose a bit more weight.

It's rush hour and the Tube and buses will be crowded so I decide to walk home through Regent's Park. On my way there, I go down Harley Street. It's gone six and the street's almost abandoned. I pass the oncology unit. The sheer white curtains on the first-floor windows are drawn. At this hour, there are no lights on. I picture the inside of the building: silent, its machines switched off and resting for the day. Today, the metal-spiralled posts outside are simply shapes.

I remember the time before I became intimate with this street. It used to be a route to the West End, or a street I'd cut across walking between the Royal Institute of British Architects and Marylebone High Street - just a connection between one segment of the city and another.

For the past year, it's been such a highly charged place. This evening it feels different, innocuous almost. I look at the purple Liberty bag on my arm and realise that once again it's simply a link between shops and park. Of course I'm relieved, but to my surprise I also find myself feeling slightly nostalgic for those strange suspended days of last summer where what mattered most was just being alive.

26

What I'm nostalgic for is the sense of remove I had from the routines and demands of everyday life last summer. I lived in my own bubble, where things like going to work, earning a living and being ambitious ceased to matter. I could justify spending time and money on massages, yoga classes, healing. It's not a place to which I ever want to return. But now, as my life slowly inches its way back to normality, there are aspects of those bittersweet days that I miss.

Cancer's made me rethink things. I'm now not sure what I want to do with my life. Architecture's interesting, but also stressful. And I don't want to go back to an office, to feel trapped by its strict rhythm and intense demands on my time. Sometimes I think about retraining as a yoga teacher or a masseuse. I'm still ambitious in that I want to be good at what I do. But most of all, I want to be happy.

Before, I wasn't really aware that life was something finite. I was young and healthy. In my mind, I had forever. Now, it seems important to spend time and energy wisely.

I tell myself these things, but I also need to be practical. Going back to an architect's office would be the obvious way to start earning again. Both Jamie, my last boss, and Anthony, my previous one, have offered me work. I'm pleased to be asked, but reluctant to be sucked back in.

Luckily, providence comes my way. In the last week of April, I get two phone calls from friends. They both want to refurbish and build extensions to their houses. Catherine knows I've been ill, Gabrielle doesn't.

'I know you're quite busy at work. Would you have time?' Gabrielle asks.

'I'm actually thinking of leaving soon as I've got some other private work.'

It's all wrong to be lying. She's actually my oldest friend. We don't see each other that often now, so it was easy not to tell her about the cancer. But it feels wrong because she's offering me an opportunity, which will mean I don't have to go back to an office, and I want to tell her how much this means to me. But I'm embarrassed telling a year on. And what if she doesn't want me to do the work once she finds out? She might worry I could get sick again.

Paola and I have decided to go to Australia in September. I put the idea to her over dinner a few weeks ago. The last time I went away for more than a couple of weeks was over a decade ago, when Julieann and I backpacked around Central America.

'How long do you want to go for?' Paola asked.

'A couple of months, ideally.'

'I couldn't do that long. Let me have a think, though.'

She called a couple of days later. 'I could come for most of September! Let's book it before we change our minds.'

The thirteenth of May marks the anniversary of my diagnosis. It's hard to believe a whole year has gone by. Each passing day takes me further away from it and is an achievement because it means I've survived longer.

I spend the afternoon in Primrose Hill, lying on the grass, feeling the coolness of the earth against my back, while the sun warms the front of my body. In the distance, I can hear the chime of the ice-cream van. The trees are now all in full blossom and the park smells of freshly mown grass. I look up at the pale blue veil of sky, criss-crossed with white vapour trails. Appearing and then dissolving, they remind me of the lines of light in a sparkler.

In a few months we'll be on our way to Australia.

Our heads are filled with plans.

'...a road trip from Cairns from Sydney...see the Barrier Reef, go to the rainforest...stop in Byron Bay on the way,' says Paola.

'Melbourne sounds cool, too. And I want to see Uluru...maybe even Perth and the West.'

When we realise how big Australia is, we decide to be less ambitious.

'Let's definitely spend a week in Byron Bay, though,' we agree.

It's an idyllic sounding beach town, south of Brisbane, where our friends Lucy and Ayala have both spent several months. They went mainly to do yoga. It's apparently nicknamed The Yoga Centre of the Western World. They described beautiful empty beaches, surrounding rainforest and the very laid-back alternative atmosphere.

The aboriginals believe the land here has powerful healing qualities, Lucy wrote in one of her emails, later adding, *Today, while having a wheatgrass shot (!), I got chatted up by a man who claims he can mend washing machines with his energy!*

I start working on my projects. At first, it's hard re-adjusting. I spend a whole day at Catherine's house in Acton doing a measured survey and come home and have to go straight to bed. It's also strange to be working alone and not having anyone to check things with. Am I doing it right? After a year's break, do I still know how to be an architect? But as with most changes, it's uncomfortable for a while and then you get used to it.

After the first couple of weeks I start to enjoy this new and less compressed rhythm of working from home, not having to get on the Tube every morning and evening and, best of all, being in charge of how I plan my day.

The timing of the trip's worked out well. Both my projects will be ready to send in for planning permission before I leave, and I'll be away during the eight weeks the local councils are supposed to take to make a decision. When I come back, the approvals will hopefully be waiting and I can start work on the detailed construction drawings.

I'm thinking several months ahead again. During treatment, I'd have felt as if this were tempting fate. Now it just happens naturally, I realise with both joy and a little trepidation.

This year I make sure I enjoy my birthday properly. Tanya and I go to yoga in the morning and have breakfast at a café in Primrose Hill. Then I go for a facial, using the spa voucher Catherine gave me for my birthday last year. I didn't want to go there while I was still wearing my wig and have to explain why. Even today I've chosen a facial rather than a massage so I can keep what's happened completely hidden. On the form I have to fill in, it asks, *Any serious illnesses?* I leave it blank. It is, I realise with relief, the first time since getting ill that I've lain on a treatment bed and not had to make reference to cancer.

After my facial I go shopping and buy some half-price shoes; beautiful tan leather high wedges, the fashion this summer. They are the first sexy shoes I've bought since I was ill. Last summer, I bought my dark brown Birkenstocks, and then in the autumn a pair of flat black Camper boots. I've worn practically nothing else.

I wear the shoes that evening when I meet my friends for dinner at The Duke of Cambridge, a gastropub in Islington. All the same people who came over last year are here again, except

Ayala, who's just had a baby. We eat on a long table in the garden and, unusually, I order steak and chips.

'No puy lentil and aubergine salad for you tonight then?' teases my friend David, relieved we're here and not in a vegetarian restaurant as I'd threatened. Tonight, there's none of the underlying sadness of last year. It's the first birthday in years where I'm actually glad to be getting older.

Paola calls the next morning. We chat about the evening for a few minutes before she says, 'I've got some news.'

From her tone of voice, happy but slightly nervous, it can only be one thing.

'You're pregnant?'

'I found out yesterday. Obviously, I didn't want to mention it in front of everyone. I'm only about four weeks.' She sounds almost apologetic. 'It was quite a shock - we weren't really trying. I'm still coming away, though.'

'Fantastic! About the pregnancy, I mean. And I'm so glad you're still coming. Though I'd understand if you didn't want to.'

'I do. I'll be three months by then. It's probably my last chance for a holiday like that.'

Since getting ill I've been invited to seven weddings and three of my closest friends - Catherine, Ayala and now Paola - have become pregnant or given birth.

When I once complained to my mother about how unfair it was that I'd got ill she said, 'No one gets through life without a rough patch. It's just that yours has happened early on.'

It's a hot summer. In the days, I'm busy working again and in the evenings I meet up with my friends, or have dinner in the garden with my parents. I'm still more tired than usual but it's no longer the drowning sense of exhaustion I carried with me throughout the winter.

'You seem lighter,' Anat says one evening. 'It was hard watching you earlier in the year and not knowing how to help make things better.' I tell her just having the support of my friends really did help. 'But like everyone said, I needed time. Although in the middle of it all, it was sometimes hard to believe things would ever change.'

By early August the temperature's topped thirty-five degrees. '...believed to be the hottest summer in over five centuries,' I hear on the radio. The nights are unbearable, as if all the heat soaked up by the city's surfaces during the day is released back into the air. Just like last year, I wake up in the middle of each night, sweating, but at least now it's for a different reason.

One night I'm in a pub with Tanya and some of her friends.

'This wine's really yellow,' someone says. 'It looks like urine.'

'Some people actually drink theirs,' says a Hungarian girl.

'How gross. Why would you do that?' asks one of the guys.

'Apparently, it can cure all sorts of things. Even cancer.'

'Come on. There's no such thing as a cure for cancer.'

Comments like this send me off balance. I can flip from thinking I'm going to be fine, to thinking it's going to come back and kill me.

On my good days, am I deluding myself? Do some cancer cells still lurk dormant in the pleasure-ground of my body? Or have they all gone away forever? Who knows.

'Breast cancer rates are definitely higher in affluent Western societies,' my surgeon once said. 'But we don't really know why. Could be diet, stress, environmental factors.'

I get really upset the day I find a printout of an email on my father's desk from a good friend of his in Chicago. He's written to say that his wife's breast cancer, in remission for over ten years, has recently come back in her liver. They're not even sure she'll make it to her daughter's wedding in the autumn. He doesn't know I've had the same disease.

I stayed with them in Chicago when I was eighteen. They were living on the top floor of a lakeside apartment block with steel-framed glass walls. They were crazy about each other. I hoped to one day have a relationship like that. But of course, the more you love someone, the more painful it is to lose them.

At times my fear's so suppressed that I think it's disappeared. But triggers like the urine comment, this email, or backache can suddenly return me to a kingdom where cancer is the ruler and the destroyer.

The fear absorbs me for a while. Luckily, it's always gone away again - the backache subsides or I'll forget what I've heard or read. There's a huge gap between these dramas I play out in my mind and what it would be like if it actually did come back. It's an unbearable thought.

In August, I find myself in another consulting room. My left knee, which I injured skiing years ago and has never been quite right since, recently became swollen and sore. I finally went to the GP who referred me to a specialist.

'It's probably because of all the yoga,' my mother tells me. 'It can be very bad for the knees.'

I tell her that's rubbish and it's more likely to be caused by the intense heat.

I'm sent for an MRI. When I walk into the building, I recognise its glacial white surfaces. It's where I had my bone scan last May. Today, the scan's in a different room on a different machine. Even I think it's highly unlikely I have cancer of the knee, but I'm still a bit anxious. It's from being in this building again, and also from knowing that the machine can reveal parts of me I know nothing about.

The consultant pins the MRI onto his light box.

'Your anterior cruciate ligament appears to be completely ruptured.'

One option is reconstructive surgery. I ask about the recovery period, enjoying talking to a doctor about a condition from which I can't possibly die.

'You'd need lots of physio after and you wouldn't be fully active for months.'

'What about stuff like yoga, skiing and hiking?'

'Probably not for at least eight months.'

He notices the look on my face.

'It's only a short while. You've got the rest of your life to do all that.'

Before, when I'd hear a comment like this I'd think, of course I do. Now, a little voice says, but I'm not exactly sure how long my life's going to be.

He asks about my general health.

'I had breast cancer last year.'

'God, you don't exactly look like someone who's had cancer.' His eyes go instantly to my chest.

A couple of weeks before Paola and I leave for Australia, I see a psychic for the first time. Chris, with whom I still occasionally have healing, told me about her. I go partly out of sheer curiosity, and also because I still find myself longing for the reassurance that there will be a future and it will be a good one. I don't necessarily think a psychic's words will be gospel, but since having met Chris I'm definitely more open to such things.

'I'll be in London next Friday,' she tells me on the phone. 'Shopping all day but you could come to my hotel room around nine.'

I walk down the long corridors of The Selfridge Hotel, looking for room 553. What if she tells me lots of bad things are going to happen? It's only the right kind of truth I want to hear.

The floor's scattered with shopping bags and the room stinks of smoke. The windows are shut as the air conditioning's on. A gold pack of B&H lie on the table.

I had an image of a plump woman with ethnic clothes, dark eyes and curly hair but Angela's in her fifties, petite with dyed blonde hair and blue eyes. She wears a simple black skirt and top.

'I hope you don't mind me smoking.' She lights up. 'It helps me concentrate when I'm doing a reading.'

She holds my silver ring in her hand, and starts talking.

'I can see red soil and funny mountains around you soon. Could be Australia.' It's a good start.

She looks at the palm of my right hand.

'You've got a very normal life line. Watch out for sciatica in that left hip.'

It is stiff, apparently connected to the knee problem.

'Can't see any other health issues, though.'

'I've had cancer,' I say wondering whether her psychic powers have actually picked this one up.

'Oh cancer,' she says, puffing on her fag. 'Don't worry about it. You're fine now. I don't get any bad vibes off you at all.'

It's exactly what I want to hear.

'Try and stay off the dairy, red meat, white flour and alcohol,' she continues, omitting to add cigarettes to the list. 'It's what I do to stay healthy.'

I ask about relationships.

'I can see your future husband around you. I don't think it's going to happen for a few years. You've got to sort everything else out first, like your work and where you're going to live. He'll be well travelled, possibly foreign. I'm getting twinkly eyes. He uses a them a lot. Beautiful hands, nice hair and an attractive but unusual face which women find fascinating. Oh, and I think he'll be rich.'

It sounds like every girl's dream.

'There'll also be someone else after you this year - it's not really serious but you'll go out with him a few times.'

I haven't even kissed anyone for over a year. Recently, I've started to sense my body coming back to life, to feel more normal again. I'm quite scared though of how a man would react if I told him I'd had cancer, particularly on a part of my body that's supposed to be sexy.

'Just don't tell,' advises my mother. 'If anyone ever asks why you've got scars just say you had a couple of benign lumps removed.'

'Do you think the fact I've had breast cancer makes me less attractive?' I ask her slightly defensively.

'Of course not. But I do think people can still be quite prejudiced and it could put some men off.'

How would I feel if I met someone who'd been through cancer? I think I'd be quite taken aback, but if I really liked him and knew the prognosis was good, I hope it wouldn't put me off. I'd be more wary if he was only recently out of treatment than if it had happened a while ago. Falling in love with someone only for them to get sick again would be awful. Though if I do ever get involved with anyone seriously, I don't think it'd be right to hide it from them.

The week before I leave for Australia, Chris invites me out for afternoon tea. It's my goodbye treat.

We sit side by side on a floral-patterned sofa in a high-ceilinged hotel drawing room eating cucumber sandwiches, scones with clotted cream, and little cakes off a three-tiered silver tray. He orders two glasses of champagne. 'I'm going to get you drunk.'

'It won't take much. I'm a very cheap date these days.'

He raises his glass.

'Here's to you, to Australia, and to our friendship.'

'And to me finding a boyfriend,' I joke. 'Perhaps you can send some good energy that way.'

'You might make me jealous.'

'Come on, don't be silly.'

'I'm serious. I've always really liked you.'

My cheeks redden with surprise.

'Really? I had no idea.'

'Well, for a start you were always going on and on about that German guy so I didn't think I had a chance. I was also meant to be helping you get better so it didn't seem quite right to cross that divide.'

I'm chuffed to know someone I found quite attractive myself liked me when I was in that state.

'So, can I persuade you to be naughty and get a room here?' he says half-jokingly.

'You're cheeky! Not today.'

My last week in London is busy. I rush around trying to finish off my work, prepare for the trip, say goodbye to friends. I move round London and realise I'm mostly back in the other world. But I can't help noticing things I never used to see. The pale young man with the vague stubble of hair who can't walk properly that I pass on Weymouth Street as I'm walking to the Royal Institute of British Architects to get a book. The bald girl being wheeled down Marylebone High Street while I sit in the sun at a pavement table at Patisserie Valerie having lunch with Julieann.

The day before we fly, I visit Aunt Ann at St Mary's. She's been in and out of hospital all year and as I've slowly become stronger, she's become weaker. A few days ago, she collapsed at home again and was re-admitted.

'She's really bad this time,' my mother said. 'You must see her before you leave.'

I take in food my mother's prepared. Mashed potato, pureed spinach, minced chicken breast. I hover the spoon in front of her. In between bird-sized mouthfuls she pauses and closes her eyes. I watch her chest continue to rise and fall, almost expecting it to stop any moment. While her eyes are shut, I stare at her face, trying to imprint it in my mind.

She's in a geriatric ward, in one of the hospital's Victorian buildings. On the other side of the room an old woman wanders round in her nightie shouting, 'She stole my bananas, she stole my bananas...'

Ann's blue eyes open again and she suddenly says, 'My darling, I'm so very proud of you. I know it hasn't been easy.'

When I say goodbye, I'm certain it's for the last time, but I don't want her to know I'm thinking that. Instead, I kiss her bony forehead, clutch her hand tightly, mutter, 'I love you,' and step out into a rain-slicked rush hour.

27

As a small child, I remember digging in the sand on beach holidays, convinced that if I kept going for long enough my spade might break through to the other side of the world and reach Australia.

Today, as I pack my bags it seems very far away. I want to separate from my recent past, yet this impending physical displacement from all that's familiar also scares me a little. My mother takes us to Heathrow. At the departure gate, I hug her several times and hold back tears as I think how much I'm going to miss seeing her almost every day, as I have done for the past year. At home, a couple of months tend to fly past. But when you go away, it sounds like such a long time.

On the journey to Sydney, we fly above Australia for several hours. Most of the land seems completely devoid of any human habitation. In several places the ground looks reddish brown, its skin rippled and pock-marked. I've never seen emptiness on such a scale. There's a beauty to it.

We approach the coastline as daylight begins to fade. Constellations of settlements appear, marking the edge between land and sea. The plane descends and they become magnified as streetlights, houses, swimming pools. Finally, there's that moment the wheels jerkily meet the ground, and I know I'm further from London than I've ever been.

I immediately feel at ease in Sydney. Walking around in the early spring heat, any thoughts of homesickness dissolve. We're staying in Darlinghurst, a nineteenth-century neighbourhood of terraced houses filled with little restaurants, cafes and boutiques. It reminds me a bit of Marylebone or Notting Hill. Sydney, though, holds no shadows.

After a week in Sydney we travel inland to the Blue Mountains. There's an out of season quietness to Katoomba, the town we're staying in, and on our walks through the eucalyptus forested landscape we see almost no one.

Then we fly to Alice Springs, in the heart of Australia, the mountains replaced by desert. Our three-day camping trip starts tomorrow.

You camping? Seriously, Annabel, I just can't see it! My friend David emails after I write to tell him our plans. *You do realise they won't have organic rocket and olive oil on the campsite!*

The minibus picks us up at six the next morning. We drive west from Alice Springs towards Ayer's Rock, or Uluru, its aboriginal name, and cut through a flat arid landscape populated by sparse desert grasses. The road is straight and the horizon never seems to shift. There are no towns or villages, only an occasional roadhouse and filling station. Every now and again a large rock formation juts out of the land, visible for miles in the surrounding emptiness.

It's raining when we get to the campsite. Square army-green tents have been placed on a patch of sandy ground where the bush's been spliced away.

David was right about the food. Beneath the drum of rain on the tarpaulin roof, white sliced bread, Kraft cheese and cold meats are passed around.

By sunset it's stopped raining but the sky's still overcast. At Uluru, along with coach-loads of other tourists, their video cameras ready, we stand holding plastic glasses of cheap wine,

214

waiting for something to happen. But the rock remains a muted terracotta, slowly darkening as the light fades.

It's too cold in the tent to sleep properly. Paola and I lie shivering on the thin narrow mattresses, consoling ourselves with images of Byron Bay, where we'll be in a couple of days, and dreaming of sunshine, beaches and mangoes.

Early in the morning we drive back to Uluru. It's raining again and no other groups have even shown up at the sunrise viewing platform. Cold and wet, we walk round the perimeter of the rock. Others have described it as a powerful experience but I'm not feeling much. It's partly the weather but I'm also disappointed by how much infrastructure there is. The viewing platforms, shops and cafes somehow spoil its essence as a lonely object in the empty landscape. And I'm learning that I'm not so good at being overwhelmed when I'm supposed to be. My own epiphanies tend to come at more unexpected, quieter moments.

The bus from Brisbane drives through the Gold Coast resorts south of the city. In the gaps between the high-rise hotels and condos that line the coastal road, I catch brief slices of ocean. Further south, the road curves inland and the landscape becomes lush and green, almost surreally bright in the afternoon sun. Along the road are signs for macadamia nut farms.

As we approach Byron Bay, the road gradually becomes fringed with caravan parks, hotels and houses. The bus drops us off on the main street in front of an Internet shop. Across the road is a giant Woolworths. Paola and I exchange glances. 'We could have stayed on Finchley Road!' I say.

Over the railway tracks, the streets are quiet with manicured front lawns and pastel timber bungalows. It reminds me of the TV soap Australia I grew up with. We ring the bell of a pale blue house with a sign saying Barbara's B&B. A blonde girl wrapped in a towel comes to the door.

'Hi I'm Jill. Barbara's not here.' She has a strong Brummie accent. 'She's accidentally double-booked your room, so you're in the cottage across the road instead. For the same price, of course.'

The cottage has white painted floorboards and a large open plan living space. There are two bedrooms, a freestanding tub in the bathroom and a small patio out the back. My bed's wide and soft and the linen smells of washing powder.

In the evening, we take a walk through the town. Many of the streets are named after writers: Burns, Byron, Lawson. The shops on Johnson, the main street, sell all the usual beach stuff like surfboards and brightly patterned shorts. But this is not your ordinary holiday town. A couple of places specialise in crystals, the community centre has a poster on its door for Kundalini dance lessons - *an ecstatic journey through the seven chakras*. The board outside the kebab shop lists tofu ones next to the lamb, and the newsagent displays meditation and yoga CDs in the window.

In a small Thai restaurant, we pick up a copy of *The Echo*, the town's free weekly and amuse ourselves by leafing through the classifieds at the back.

'Fancy some Tantric Tibetan Healing?' I ask Paola. '"Powerful energy work specialising in sexual issues."'

They even have astrology readings for pets.

After dinner, we check our emails at the Internet shop. The camp-looking guy behind the counter with bleached hair, a pierced nose and English accent looks vaguely familiar. He keeps staring at me.

Eventually, he comes over.

'Don't I know you from somewhere? London?'

Now I recognise his voice from over a decade ago.

'You're Adam. We met through Pippa.' He was at The Slade art school with my friend. Back then, he had dark brown hair, no piercings and wore brogues.

'So, what are you doing here?' I ask.

'I've been in Australia about eighteen months. I was sick of England and needed to get out.'

He gives me his number, suggesting we have coffee.

Paola and I spend a week together in Byron Bay. Our days have a relaxed rhythm. Breakfast in our backyard followed by a late morning yoga class and afternoons on the beach. At our first class the teacher told Paola she couldn't believe she was four months pregnant as she was so strong and hardly showed.

'Do you think there's something wrong with the baby?' she asked me, momentarily worried.

'Of course not. And think how much you'd have hated it if she'd said you looked big.'

When it's time for Paola to go home, I take her to the bus station. Then I go back to the cottage and pack my bags and move out of the cottage and into a small single room at the B&B.

I miss Paola as soon as she's gone. I go to yoga but it feels empty without her on the next mat. I sit alone in the organic café we often went to, aware of her absence in the empty chair opposite, the single glass of carrot juice on the table. By now she must be on the plane and I'm wishing, in some ways, I'd gone with her. I spend the rest of the day aimlessly wandering round town, not quite sure why I've chosen to stay alone here, on the other side of the world. Later, I stop by the Internet shop. Adam's working today and it's a relief to see a familiar face.

'Everything OK?' he asks. 'You seem a bit down.'

'I'm feeling slightly lost. My friend went back to England today.'

'Tell you what, I'm not working tomorrow. Let's do breakfast. Say Espressoheads at eleven.'

I'm excited to find eight new messages in my inbox. I open David's first. It's a reply to the one I sent him about our camping trip and I'm sure it's going to make me laugh.

Things here haven't been too great, he writes. *N's dad just got diagnosed with Hodgkin's. He's starting high dose chemotherapy next week.*

I'm really upset for David's wife. And hearing about someone else getting cancer also makes me scared again.

'Why did you leave England?' I ask Adam the next day.

'The last few years were fucking awful. First, I lost my father to cancer. Then less than two years later my half-sister got Hodgkin's disease. We thought she'd gone into remission but it came back. She was dead at forty. Not long after, my mother died. Basically, from a broken heart.'

'I'm so sorry. It must have been unbelievably hard. Must still be. How are you now?'

'Up and down. I still seem to spend far too much time getting wasted. It's the only way I can really handle it. It seems like the whole fucking world's got cancer. I get home from work a few weeks ago and - can you believe it - my housemate tells me she's just been diagnosed with breast cancer. At twenty-nine. Now she's on chemo and moping round the house totally depressed. I just can't seem to get away from this disease.'

Neither can I. I wasn't going to tell anyone here about mine. I don't want to be another person to add to Adam's list but I can't sit here having this conversation and pretend it's something that hasn't affected my own life.

'I've had breast cancer, too.'

Now he's shocked. 'God, how shit for you.'

'I know. It was caught early so I'm keeping my fingers crossed. Of course, I still worry.'

'It must be awful living with the fear that it could come back.'

My friends have always said things like, *I just know everything's going to be fine,* or, *I've got a really good vibe.* But Adam knows that things don't always work out the way you hope.

Our conversation is interrupted by three pretty blonde Australian girls who sit down at our table. 'Hey, Adam, how's it going? We missed you at C-Moog last night.'

'I was still hung over so I stayed in. This is my friend Annabel from London. Annabel meet Laura, Honey, and Amy.'

'Nice to meet you.' Honey smiles briefly before turning back to Adam. 'Are you coming out later? There's a rave in a field near Bangalow.'

'I'm definitely up for a big one tonight. Do you want to come?' he asks me.

It's the last thing I want to do. So far from everyone who matters to me and surrounded by all these stories of cancer, I feel isolated and vulnerable. Being in a field full of ravers would only make me more so. After I leave Adam and the girls, I walk down the main street and watch all the tourists. They're mostly young, here to have a good time and party, and look as if they haven't a care in the world.

I long to be like that, too. I have to remind myself that appearances can often be deceptive. If you saw Adam in his ripped T-shirt showing off his beach body, singing along to 'Dancing Queen' behind the shop counter, you'd never guess what he's been through.

The first couple of days by myself are lonely. I walk round feeling awkward, a nervy uncomfortable sensation in my stomach, as if my body's literally been put in the wrong place. Although it's sunny and there are beautiful beaches, I miss home. It's the end of September and I long to see the leaves turning colour and the days getting shorter. I always thought I was quite independent and someone who enjoyed spending time alone. But now I realise I loved those times precisely because they were so finite.

I call my mother, hoping her voice will soothe me. I say I'm having a good time as otherwise she'll start fussing. We talk about Aunt Ann who amazingly has improved and been able to leave hospital. 'Old weeds never die,' she used to say.

Then my mother tells me that Jamie died. He's the brother of a family friend, the one diagnosed with kidney cancer about three years ago. He died aged thirty-four, leaving a wife and a young son.

'I wasn't sure whether to tell you on the phone,' she says.

'I kind of wish you hadn't.' I don't mention David's father-in-law or Adam.

I'm really upset, both for everyone who's lost Jamie, and for myself, for having had this illness. It hurts most to hear of someone young dying from it. I have to force myself to remember that our situations were different. His had already spread to his bones when it was found, mine was a local tumour.

I start getting used to being alone, and begin to enjoy it. I recognise that it's a brief luxury. Soon I'll be back at my desk, drawing on the computer in the winter rain, and I know I'll look back with longing on these days where all I did was yoga, go to the beach, read and sit in lovely cafes.

Every afternoon I cycle down to my favourite beach, Belongil, just outside the town centre. It's usually almost empty. I lie down and close my eyes, aware only of the sensation of the warm sand and sun on my skin and the sound of the surf slapping the shore. Floating on the sea, buoyed gently up and down by the waves, I realise I'm at ease in my skin again.

The B&B owner tells me I'll have to leave by the end of the week as she's fully booked. I need to decide whether to stay in Byron Bay or go off travelling. Part of me wants to see some other places, but I'm also now enjoying the relaxed pace here. And there's a month-long yoga course I'm keen to do. It's in *Ashtanga* Yoga, which I've never tried. Ayala did the same course while she was here and emailed to say how amazing it was.

It's not easy to find new accommodation. Eventually, I find space at a B&B called A Peaceful Place run by a South African couple in their fifties called Stan and Zeta. He's a stained-glass artist, she is a reiki and crystal healer. Zeta shows me a sunny room with a huge picture of an angel above the bed.

'This room has a special energy, because of the angel,' she says. How very Byron.

Their esoteric vibe seems at odds with the rather stringent house rules:

Showers must last no longer than five minutes. You must wipe all traces of water off the floor with the specially provided cloth. No cooking after 8pm. No visitors allowed in rooms.

If I want to stay and do the yoga course, I'll have to put up with the angel and the quick showers.

Once I've made the decision, I start to meet a few people. After a Saturday morning yoga class, I'm invited along to breakfast in a nearby café with a few people. I get talking to a very skinny, suntanned American girl, with a pierced belly button, called Delia.

'Spencer and I are going to the Beach House tonight for drinks,' she says pointing to an earnest looking dark-haired man. 'Come with us.'

In the bar, before Spencer arrives, I learn she's from Phoenix, Arizona and recently divorced. 'I was thirty-three, working as a teacher, trapped in a dead-end marriage in this conservative little town. I thought, is this really it? So I'm spending six months here enjoying the yoga and the men.' She starts telling me about all the different guys she's slept with, listing English, Swiss and Italian among her conquests, their bedroom abilities apparently rated in ascending order. She asks if I've met anyone yet and I feel rather boring saying no.

'What about you and Spencer?' I try and shift the attention off me.

'I think he'd like there to be. He's a bit tortured, though. I like 'em young and fun.'

Spencer turns up. Also from the States, he used to be a naturopath. Now he's working part-time in a shop while trying to find himself. 'I think I'm getting very close.'

Most days I have lunch on the terrace at Fundamental Foods. It's a health food store with a cafe, selling chickpea salads, brown rice and avocado sushi, smoothies. It's perfect for the healthy diet I still mostly stick to. I'm looking for a space on the crowded terrace one lunchtime when a man says, 'Do you want to share with us?'

They introduce themselves as Dave, Sol and Will. Dave and Sol look like well-preserved fifty-year-olds, Will a bit younger. Dave's got dyed blonde hair, mirrored sunglasses and his left bicep has a tattoo of a heart inscribed with the word *Surrender*.

'So what do you all do?'

'I'm a counsellor - sexual and relationship stuff,' says Dave. 'I haven't actually done much since about ninety-eight. I think I might be ready to start again soon, though.'

He's a little surprised when I ask why the career break. 'I just wasn't quite in the right space for it. I needed some time to myself.'

Dave hands me his card. It has gold lettering on a turquoise background. 'The colour of my star sign, Sagittarius,' he explains. Sol passes his over. Sprinkled with gold glitter, it lists his many talents: *Artist, Philosopher, Psychic, Counsellor, Photographer, Guru.* And, last but not least, *God.*

'They're lovely.' I try and keep a straight face.

'I spend most of my time hanging out at our house in the hills,' explains Sol. 'It's got a three-sixty-degree view of the ocean. Come by sometime and we can get up early to watch the sunrise.'

They're nice and friendly but I'm not sure I fancy a sleepover.

I run into them most lunchtimes. None of us have much to do so we linger on the terrace drinking dandelion soya lattes (known here as LSDs) and chatting. I'm happy to have people to talk to, and curious to be encountering types I'd never have come across in London.

Sol tells me he was a company director in South Africa but, 'After my marriage broke down I came here. Will and I met in the toilets at a nudist music festival a few years back.'

'That's certainly an unusual place to meet.'

'We've even got photos to prove it,' says Will.

'It's OK, I believe you.'

Will's just come out of eighteen months' drug and alcohol rehab in Sydney. Dave also used to be into drugs, alcohol and sex. 'But since I split with my last girlfriend - she was always pissed - I've been celibate and clean.'

'When was that?' I expect him to say a few months.

'Almost four and a half years ago.'

Even I've only been celibate for a couple. I'm glad to hear someone's broken my record.

They want to know about life in London.

'It's an amazing place. So many different kinds of people and things to do. Though sometimes it can seem a bit manic and overcrowded.'

'So, you mean people don't really make much time for themselves?' asks Sol.

'Not like here. You do feel as if people are always rushing from one thing to the next. Everything - whether it's the gym or meeting for a coffee - seems to have a little time slot marked out for it.'

'Do you think people can really be happy like that?' asks Dave. 'My guru says, "So much time is spent on other responsibilities, leaving little or no time to attend to the need within. Yet when some attention is given to the inner self, the door of joy is opened."'

It's a hard balance. I couldn't spend the rest of my life just hanging out, navel and sunrise-gazing. But nor do I want to go back to my old one, of constantly rushing, always feeling overloaded. I want a life that's interesting and stimulating yet one that allows for space and quiet moments.

I start the *Ashtanga* course. It's hard work. What I love is how every morning before we begin the yoga poses, Dena, our teacher, leads us through a meditation. She instructs us to try and stay present and focused on each breath rather than letting our minds constantly jump into the past and the future.

Ashtanga's different from the kind of yoga I've done before. Even though many of the poses are familiar, what's new is how you jump between them and keep repeating a *vinyasa*, a series of flowing movements from and back into downward dog pose, which uses your whole body strength. By the end of the first week, I'm exhausted and all my muscles ache. But I'm also exhilarated. It feels great to be challenging my body again. Even though I did yoga most of the way through my treatment and recovery, I was careful not to overexert myself. There's now something magical about moving through these very fluid and graceful postures and in feeling my body twist, fold, sweat and breathe.

I'm in a shop buying fruit when a guy with blonde dreadlocks and an American accent comes up to me.

'Hey, how're you doing?' he says.

By now I'm used to this kind of friendliness from strangers.

'Saw you down the market on Sunday in the chai tent. You seemed to be enjoying the drumming. I'm Sean, by the way.'

I hadn't spotted him among the market crowds. But now I look at him and notice his bright blue eyes and very toned body and think, a bit grungy but quite cute.

'I'm Annabel.'

'I take it you're English?'

'I am. From London.'

'What a place. I lived there for four years. It was a total blast. I worked in a health food shop in Kings Cross. We should go for a chai sometime. It'd be great to reminisce about my favourite city with you.'

28

I'm drinking tea in the garden at Espressoheads a few days later when I hear an American accent.

'Hey, can I join you? This is where I work.' Sean sits down before I've had a chance to respond.

'In the café?' I'm surprised as I come here most days and have never seen him.

'No, the shed at the back. I'm a masseur.'

'Where did you learn that?' I expect him to say on a two-week course while stoned on a beach in Thailand.

It turns out to be somewhere called the Esalen Institute, in Big Sur, California, which, he tells me, is unique in combining Swedish massage with Gestalt Therapy. I don't know much about either but it sounds more serious than I'd have expected. For several years he was head masseur at a very posh West Coast spa.

'I had to have my hair real short back then.' He touches a beaded dreadlock. 'I'd get up at five every day to do yoga. For seven years I ate only raw. London fucked all that up, though.'

'Why?'

'I came over to go to Glastonbury. It was the first time I'd left the States. Ended up staying four years. Lived in this squat in Islington. I went a bit wild. Started clubbing and boozing. Even ate a few kebabs. You'd never have recognised me. Thigh-length Doc Martens and black PVC trousers.'

We both laugh. I can't imagine our paths having crossed there, or if they had, that we'd have shown the slightest interest in one another.

We chat for almost two hours, about yoga, meditation, food, religion, our different lives and cultures. He tells me he loves his work, something I always find attractive. It's surprisingly easy spending time with him.

'I like you Brits,' he says. 'The humour and eccentricity. Americans are much more straight-laced.'

'What, like you!?'

'Ah, but I grew up on a commune in California.'

A world away from my Primrose Hill childhood.

He leaves, saying he wants to get a surf in before the sun goes down. I'm happy when he asks if I want to meet up the following afternoon.

Today, Sean's wearing bright red Thai fisherman's trousers and a saffron vest, his feet bare. I've never been drawn to someone this unconventional. Here, my London priorities slip away. I'm not thinking about whether I could spend the rest of my life with him, but just enjoying his company.

After tea, he shows me his massage space. It's a green shed tucked behind the café garden. A blackboard announces The House of Healing in swirling coloured chalk letters. Inside is a simple room with a wooden floor, white walls, a massage bed. It smells of jasmine.

'This place has great energy,' he says. 'Everyone comments. I specially clean it with my aura each week.'

'I'll remember that next time I don't feel like hoovering.'

He looks momentarily confused, then laughs. 'Oh, you mean vacuuming. I'm serious, though.'

It's interesting how some spaces, such as this, do just feel right, even if they're not the most beautiful ones. Perhaps it's to do with the energy and mood of the people who inhabit them. Conversely, I've been in the most visually exquisite spaces, which have felt cold and edgy.

Sean opens a door. 'And this is where I live.'

A pile of clothes, a couple of papayas and a guitar lie on the floor next to the mattress. What would it be like to spend the night here with him?

I sit down on the massage bed while Sean prepares the room for his next client. He lights incense and candles and re-arranges his crystals. Then he stands next to me and slowly runs his hand down my neck, my shoulder and my arm, waking up my skin. It's a beautiful hand, tanned with slim fingers and defined knuckles and joints. I remember my mother once saying, 'Hands are so important. Never go out with someone who has ugly ones.'

There's a knock on the door and a male voice calls out, 'Hey, Sean.'

'That's my client,' he says. 'Do you want to come for a massage tomorrow afternoon? My treat.'

'Sure. That sounds great.'

In London I'd never go round to some guy's place I'd just randomly met for a massage. And I've never had a massage from a man with whom some chemistry could be brewing.

Sean hugs me when I arrive. Then he turns professional.

'I'll go out of the room while you get undressed. Take off as much as you're comfortable with and lie on your front with the sheet over you.'

I take my skirt and vest top off and hesitate before removing my bra. Most masseurs prefer you to take it off and I don't want him to think I'm prudish or ill at ease. But neither do I want him to see my scars. I just hope the sheet will keep them hidden.

Sean comes back in, folds over the sheet and places his oiled hands at the base of my back. They start to move, lightly at first,

228

gliding up and down my spine, across my shoulders and neck. Then he works his fingers deeper, pressing into the flesh. They know exactly where to go, reaching into all the tight places, squeezing out the tension. We are both silent. The only sounds are his breath and the subtle brush of oiled skin meeting skin.

He asks me to turn over, holding the sheet above me as I rotate. Lying on my back, I feel more exposed. His hands move across my scalp, then smooth out my forehead, cheekbones and jaw.

My eyes are closed but does my face gives away the mix of pleasure and slight awkwardness that his touch rouses in me? I want to just lose myself in the sensations but can't help feeling self-conscious. What's he thinking as his hands travel across my body? Am I a woman he likes, or just a construction of muscle, bone and flesh to be worked on?

He reaches the ridges of my collarbones and then dips down towards the curve of my sternum. The sheet, which had until now kept me covered, starts to slip away. I open my eyes very slightly, relieved to see his are closed and he seems lost in the meditative state he told me he often went into when he was working.

Suddenly, the sheet's gone and his hands are sliding across the top of my breasts, skimming just above the nipples. Michelle did that too, but today my body tenses. His breath's now deepened. I look out through slitted eyes. His, thankfully, are still shut.

When he's finished, he drapes the sheet back over me and quietly leaves the room.

'How are you?' he asks when he comes back in.

'That was lovely.'

I'm hoping he'll say something about how great it was to work on my body.

'Your back and shoulders felt real tight. I think you're still carrying a bit of London. The other thing, which surprised me, was I could feel some sadness, some grief in you. I couldn't figure that one out, though. Shall we go for a drink?'

'I can't tonight. How about tomorrow?' I feel like being alone.

I cycle towards the beach. The sun's almost down when I get there, only a faint rim of orange lingers around the hills. I sit down on the now cool sand, that prickly feeling in the back of my eyes. I thought my sadness had gone. But perhaps feelings, like cancer cells, can hide inside us and we don't even realise they're there. I stay on the beach until the light's gone and the shoreline, no longer visible, is registered only by the soothing sound of the waves.

The following evening, Sean and I meet at The Rails, a bar next to the station where everyone seems to congregate. We're both drinking mineral water through pink and white stripy straws. For once he seems almost tongue-tied and just sits there smiling.

Jill, the girl from Birmingham I met at the first B&B, comes over, breaking the silence.

'Hi, guys. Didn't realise you knew each other.'

'Are you seeing him?' she asks when he's at the bar getting us more drinks.

'We're friends.'

'He's quite sound, you know. Especially compared to most of the losers round here.'

'I feel very drawn to you,' he says once Jill's gone. Today, his words make me smile inside. He takes my hand and we sit there, still not saying much, as the music plays and people continuously move around us.

Later, he cycles me home. Gliding through the backstreets side-by-side, all I can hear is the whir of our bikes and the hum of cicadas.

Under the vast Australian sky, I am finally kissed again.

'Goodnight, beautiful,' he eventually says. 'I'm going to sleep so well tonight.'

I lie in bed, replaying the kiss in my head. It was a good one, but best of all it feels like a doorway, closed for a long time, has finally opened again.

I run into Sean on the main street the next day. In the midst of all the Saturday crowds, we start kissing again. He's just been for a surf and his skin tastes of salt.

'Shall we meet up later?' he asks. 'Maybe take a walk down the beach, go for dinner?' He's doing massages all afternoon and says he'll call when he's done. At eight, fed up with waiting, I switch my phone off.

A couple of years ago, Ioana and I read *The Rules*, a dating guide, which tells you to play it cool. Very cool. Never accept a Saturday night date after Wednesday, and to be sure keep an egg-timer by your phone and end phone calls after ten minutes, it instructed. Even though I thought it was completely over the top, I do tend to err on the cool side.

I go out for dinner with some yoga friends and later, when I check my voicemail, I discover Sean left a message at eight-thirty, wanting to meet up. As he doesn't have a phone, I can't call him back.

'What happened to you on Saturday?' he says when I bump into him at Fundamental Foods on Monday morning.

'I didn't hear from you so I went and did something else.'

'I'm really sorry I left it so late. I'm not so good at this making arrangements stuff. Prefer to do things spontaneously. Live in the moment.'

I watch him spoon spirulina and bee pollen into his smoothie, from little jars he's taken out of a battered brown leather satchel.

'I agree. But I also think if you never make plans you can miss out on stuff.'

What I don't add is that in some ways I actually wish I could be more like him. He seems to move through life so much more fluidly, without constantly planning and overanalysing, like me.

'You're such a London girl,' he laughs putting his arms round me. 'I think the universe brings things to people when their energy's right for it. Like today - it's fate we ran into each other.'

I don't mention it's not such a massive coincidence, given we both come in here at least once a day. I saw him in here twice last week.

We carry on spending time together, but it's always random and unplanned.

'You and I could have a really wild time,' he says one afternoon while we're eating mangoes on the terrace at the health food shop. He kisses me, his mouth sweet with juice.

Maybe we could. Sometimes I wish we were doing. But much as I enjoy his company, I'm not sure I'm ready for something deeper, or if that's what he even wants. I think we're both quite fascinated by the other, yet something holds us back. Perhaps for me, this intimate friendship is enough right now. And if I did fall in love, it would be all the harder to leave.

In mid-November, the *Ashtanga* course finishes. I've become stronger each week, the eternal *vinyasa* now manageable. I'm able to stand on my head, and balance on my arms with my legs wrapped around them in a pose called *Bhujapidasana*. This yoga, with its particular deep breathing designed to build heat, is intense. But it makes me feel so alive. It's such a contrast to last November, lying on the sofa wrapped in a blanket, watching daytime TV.

On the final day of the course, we all thank Dena, our teacher.

'I should be thanking you,' she says. 'I love doing this. If there's one piece of advice I can give it's always go with your instinct and do what feels authentic to you.'

I know I'll hold on to Dena's words, spoken in her soft Australian accent, her blue eyes radiant as she sits in lotus position on the dark wood floor of her yoga studio.

There are other words I also remember from this period of my life.

She's now playing better than ever, the anaesthetist at the hospital said, describing the world-famous pianist who also had breast cancer. Then, his words sounded ridiculous. Now, I realise it is possible to go beyond what you were before.

This illness will take eighteen months out of your life, the breast care nurse at the oncology unit said to me last summer as I sat in an armchair, the drugs dripping into me. It has been exactly eighteen months.

Byron is starting to change. School's finished and teenagers flood in, breaking up the tranquil mood. Almost overnight, accommodation prices double. Even though here spring is ripening, I think I'm ready to go home.

Gabrielle calls from London to tell me the planning permission for her house has just come through from Camden Council. To our amazement, it's on time. I picture the town hall on Judd Street in King's Cross, planning officers in rubber-soled shoes moving soundlessly across its carpeted floors. It's a very different King's Cross to the one Sean knew: Tony's Hemp Corner on the Caledonian Road by day, The Cross club in the goods yard, north of the station, by night.

Gabrielle's excited, saying she can't wait for me to start doing the detail drawings. I'm looking forward to bringing my first solo project to life: to realising the large glass sliding doors opening to a decked courtyard, the six-metre skinny roof-light dropping light onto a white wall.

I'll be sad to let go of these warm, slow-paced days, although I never intended them to last forever. Occasionally, I do have fantasies about staying: taking Dena's *Ashtanga* teacher-training course, falling in love with Sean, living in the hills together, having children, and preparing raw food feasts.

That appeals to part of me, but there's a stronger pull towards my home: to my city with its history, culture and diversity, where a heritage building does not mean a fifties prefab, and where there will always be places I've yet to discover.

I'm even starting to miss the food in London. At first, I couldn't get enough of the tropical fruit, fresh juices, tofu and exotic salads. Now, I'm looking forward to mash, a curry, apple crumble and custard.

But I hope I'll take back some of the relaxed openness of this life to my exciting, but sometimes overwhelming city. I remember the diary entry I wrote just before I got ill. *I wish I had more time. Time to look after myself, to be still, to do things like meditation.* I've done plenty of these the last eighteen months. And I want to do plenty more. But I also want to work, have fun, buy a flat, stay up late, meet someone.

According to Stan, the B&B owner, Byron changes people. He tells me the story of a very proper English girl who, after a week was discovered eating breakfast topless in his garden.

'What about you?' he asks.

I make a joke about my *Ashtanga*-toned arms, explaining how we had to do that *vinyasa* about fifty times a day. It has given me a confidence in my body I haven't had in a while.

In the meditation we did at the beginning of each yoga class, Dena always talked about keeping your mind present, rather than letting it drift off to the past or future. It's hard to do, but it reminds me there's no point being constantly burdened by your past or afraid of your future. It's better to just try and let life unfold day-by-day.

Spending time away from London and all its memories of illness has helped create some distance from that experience. Gradually, I'm feeling less and less defined as someone who had cancer. I've seen how many ways there are to live your life. And it's reaffirmed that most important of all is to find the ones that make you happy.

Unusually, it pours continuously for three days just before I leave. The rain reminds me of London and, for the first time in weeks, makes me homesick. Rain doesn't suit Byron. I can't go to the beach and find myself shivering in soaking summer clothes. It's a month before Christmas and suddenly I long for warm cafes with steamed-up windows, woolly coats damp with the smell of rain. Chris texts me, as he's done every few weeks. *London's waiting for you doll. Xx.*

On my last day, the rain stops and the town and beach come back to life. I run into Sean outside Espressoheads. I haven't seen him since the rain began.

'I'm going back to London tomorrow.'

He looks surprised, disappointed even. 'I thought you'd end up staying a while. This place seems to suit you.'

'I like it a lot, but I'm ready to go back.'

'Let's get a chai.' We walk into the cafe garden and sit down at the same table where a few weeks ago we had our first proper conversation. Today, he seems a bit down and tells me business is slow.

'The universe just isn't providing at the moment. I've only done one massage all week. All I've eaten today is half a papaya.'

I remember his comment about the universe bringing you things when the time was right.

'Perhaps you're out of alignment with your true path.' I'm only half-joking.

'Can I ask you something real personal?' he says while we're drinking our tea.

'Sure. What?'

'Those scars on your chest. What are they? Have you had a boob job or something?'

I didn't think he'd noticed. And especially having lived in California, he ought to know that boob job scars are discretely placed on the underside, not slashed across the middle of your breasts.

'I actually had cancer.'

'You're kidding. When?'

'Eighteen months ago.'

He tells me how sorry he is.

'In my work I've come across lots of people who've had cancer. I think if there's one thing it teaches you, it's how to really love yourself.'

'It has made me realise how precious my life is.'

'I'm sure we'll see each other again somewhere, sometime,' he says when we kiss each other goodbye. As he strokes my back I feel sad, knowing we almost certainly won't, and that what we shared, light as it was, actually did matter to me.

I wake from a brief sleep. The screen in front of my seat indicates we're near Kabul. I look out of the window. A clear, crisp winter light falls over barren mountains. Only an occasional road leading to a single village scars the landscape. We glide above places I'll never set foot in and I think about how, in our short lives, most of us only ever get to experience such a tiny sliver of this world.

We are flying backwards through time. I look at the screen. It's seven-thirty in the morning in London. I picture my mother standing in the kitchen in her white dressing gown with the frayed sleeves, her slippered feet just feeling the heat breathing through the now cracked terracotta tiles. Her breath smudges the windowpane, as she looks out across the still dark garden, thinking how in a few hours it'll be time to leave for the airport.

The stewardess rolls her trolley stacked with plastic breakfast trays down the aisle. 'Tea or coffee...coffee or tea...' I look at my watch again. Still another couple of hours to go. As this plane carries me home, I reflect back over the past eighteen months. How will their sediment settle?

We drop through the clouds. A grey spine of water twists beneath me. We pass over marshlands and sewage works, the docks, St Paul's, Waterloo Station, Richmond Park.

It has been a long journey home.

29

'Triple negative breast cancer is unlikely to return once it's stayed quiet this long,' says Dr Jones, my oncologist. It is April 2007, and five years since my diagnosis.

'Your chances of getting secondary breast cancer are now very low,' she continues.

'What about my odds of a new primary one?'

'Around the same as the average woman.'

'So I'm pretty much back to normal?'

'You are.'

'Great.'

I've been waiting so long to hear these words. Five years ago, I doubted they'd even be possible. But today they don't fully reach me.

'And how's everything else going? Anyone special in your life?' my doctor asks, as she does every year. This time, I envisaged myself saying yes.

I start crying.

Dr Jones, so well versed in empathy for the fear and sadness of cancer, looks bewildered. I dab my eyes with a tissue from the box on her desk. She can't find her words, and I'm embarrassed. There are probably people on her list today who are terminally ill.

As I'm leaving, she comes out with, 'I do hope you find someone who appreciates your worth.'

I go past the waiting room on my way out. Inside, sit a woman with no hair and a man in a wheelchair. The woman looks at my tear-stained face. I can guess what she's thinking.

Until a week ago, I thought I had found someone. We meet at a New Year's Eve party, at a restaurant called Indigo in Mumbai. It is the start of a two-week holiday to India that I'm taking with four friends. We are all dancing when a tall handsome Indian man approaches me. I assume he's local, but it turns out he is from London too, also on holiday with his friends, except he's at the end of his stay and heading home the next day.

We text back and forth while I am in Goa and when I return, we meet up again at a bar in Smithfield market. I learn he's the finance director of a church conservation charity. I like that his work supports beautiful buildings. Soon we are seeing one another a few times a week. A couple of months in, I host a dinner party at my flat on a Saturday night and introduce him to Paola and Anat and their partners. We spend the next day wandering around Tate Modern, enjoying the *Gilbert & George* exhibition and sitting in the Members' Room chatting for ages over tea and scones. It is a perfect weekend, the kind I had long dreamt of. Could this be the man I might spend the rest of my life with? Was the magical way we met destiny pulling us together?

Two days later, we get together after work. Over red wine at the Coach & Horses pub in Soho, he announces, 'I can't do this anymore.'

'What. Why not?'

'You're the first person I've met in a long time who I could imagine settling down with. But my parents have no idea I date white women. They want me to marry someone Indian. My mum keeps giving me girls' numbers.'

But by the end of the evening, he's changed his mind again.

239

'I decided before I arrived tonight it was best I didn't see you again. But now I'm with you, I realise I don't want to have to let you go.'

I give him another chance.

A couple of weeks later, on Good Friday, I am walking along the Boating Lake in Regent's Park, en route to St George's on Hanover Square, where my family and I go each year to hear the *St Matthew* Passion. It is April 6th, a date I always remember, because it's the one on which I found the lump. I'm admiring the clumps of daffodils on the grass alongside the lake and enjoying the sunshine against my skin on this unseasonably hot day. I feel deeply grateful to be alive. My phone rings.

'It's me,' he says. 'I'm so sorry, but I've had another change of heart. I just can't do this after all.'

When I hang up, I am furious about having given him another chance. Furious he had to go and ruin this, of all days. For once, I am unable to enjoy Bach's beautiful music.

Aside from this hurt, life is good. I've been living in my flat in Primrose Hill for a year. I never intended to be at my parents' as long as I was. However, treatment, recovery, the trip to Australia, a long slow search for the perfect place, and almost as long and slow a gestation of its transformation from wreck to dream space (courtesy of capricious Polish builders) meant I stayed there almost four years.

I adore my new home's high ceilings and huge bay window with a view over my neighbour's long wild garden. It is where I spend much of my time, as I work from there as a freelance architect, getting my own projects, mostly through word of mouth. I relish the freedom my work gives me and don't miss the structure of being in an office. I love how, deadlines permitting, I can sometimes go to daytime yoga classes or meet a friend for lunch. Or choose to work all day Saturday and take Wednesday off.

My passion for yoga keeps growing. After I returned from Australia, I still found myself wanting to practice it every day. I was always reading books on yoga and would regularly take workshops with international teachers when they travelled to London. It felt completely natural to start an eighteen-month yoga teacher-training at the end of 2006. I'm doing it at Triyoga, the studio I practice at, and where I first fell in love with yoga. We meet once a month, and they are long intense weekends where we learn about the poses, the philosophy, the anatomy, the art of teaching. And in between, there is lots to study. My body is now stronger than ever. When I move through the beautiful forms of the yoga poses, sickness, and the deep fear my body once carried, are unremembered.

I decide to try online dating, and sign up for Guardian Soulmates. Chris the healer, with whom I am still friends, comes over and takes some photos of me standing by my bay window in a pair of tight jeans. I receive a fair amount of attention when I first join. I decide to keep as open a mind as possible. Possibly too open. My first date is with an Italian art historian turned film producer whose photo is extremely blurred. We meet at a hotel bar on Sloane Street and I learn my first lesson of online dating: try and get a sense of what they actually look like before you agree to meet up. When he announces, 'I have a pet ferret. She usually sleeps in my bed,' I know for sure this one is a non-starter. I don't fancy a threesome with a ferret.

My second date is with an award-winning photographer, who has photos in the National Portrait Gallery. My Talented Artist Who Also Loves To Cook fantasy rapidly dissolves as we sit in a Turkish restaurant in Waterloo and he spends the entire evening telling me about the depression he's been suffering from since his partner left him.

I come into contact with all sorts. There's the English actor in LA who's planning to move back to the UK. We chat on the phone and he tells me he's tired of the eternally good weather and women who refuse to eat proper meals. He asks for my birth date and time and I hear the tap of his fingers across the keyboard. 'I'm doing our composite birth charts. With your Venus in Leo and my Mars in Aries, we'd have a fantastic sex life. Women here, they don't like sex much, either.' By the time he starts rambling on about 9/11 conspiracy theories, I have checked out.

There are also encounters with men such as the guy from Sao Paolo who studied at London School of Economics and works for the Brazilian World Service. While we both enjoy hearing about one another's worlds, I can sense neither of us will try and take things further. There's the gorgeous psychologist I meet at a canal side pub in Islington on a warm July night, and I come away convinced I have met my soulmate. When I get off the Tube at Chalk Farm, he's already texted to say how much he loved our evening and can we please meet again next week. Then he disappears. Which, I soon learn, can happen all too easily in the cyber world.

These days, my anxieties are more likely to be about a guy I like not texting back, or the builder phoning up to say there's a problem on site with the setting out of the stone for a bathroom vanity unit, and that I need to get down there as soon as possible.

I don't spend much time thinking about cancer. In fact, I'm more likely to worry about ageing than about dying young. And now, I dare to dream about the future.

TWO

30

I find him on a cold December night at the end of 2009. I am still signed up to Guardian Soulmates. The two plus years I've been on there have yielded a few short relationships, but no one with the potential to become a life partner. This Friday evening, a couple of weeks after the end of my most recent 'relationship', I'm not feeling at my most hopeful as I search the website for potentials. I scroll through thumbnail image after image, each accompanied by a name, an age and a location. Most, I don't bother clicking on to find out more.

I do bother when I come across *Hedge,* aged forty, from London. He has light-brown wavy hair, huge blue eyes and is a bit rugged looking. I read his full profile and it's clear he is intelligent - he does something mathematical in the city. He's also a keen photographer and loves art. And his profile makes me laugh as it includes a few multiple-choice questions for potential dates, such as, *What shoes would you wear out on a date with me? Doc Martens, stripper shoes, or a nice elegant pair of heels?*

I click on his additional photos. There's one of him on a beach somewhere, laughing as he takes a photo with an old-fashioned camera, his face, with its aquiline nose, seen side-on. I want to be with this man, I think to myself. It is of course a totally irrational thought, as I have no idea what kind of a person he is. In fact, he strikes me as possibly being a bit pretentious.

I put him in my Favourites. Over Christmas, we email back and forth. I tell him I haven't worn Doc Martens since I was a teenager and if he's expecting stripper shoes, there are probably more suitable websites than Soulmates for that sort of thing. He is up north with his family over the holiday period so we arrange to meet in early January. He suggests a Middle Eastern bar and restaurant called Mamounia Lounge on Curzon Street.

Let's have a drink, he emails. *And if after an hour we can still stand the sight of one another, we could have dinner, too.*

'Odds are this will come to nothing,' I tell my mother as I walk from Green Park Tube to the bar. I am wearing flat black boots.

Hedge, whose real name is Mark, does actually look like his photographs, though in person he's quieter and thankfully less pretentious than he appeared online. I find out he trained as an engineer and lived in the Lake District for a few years before doing an MBA and moving to London. He's been married before, but doesn't have children.

'So, shall we have something to eat?' I'm pleased to hear him say, once we've finished our cocktails.

Over tagines, I tell him how I like writing, and he says he's helped a friend edit her books.

'What kind of books does she write?'

'Erotic fiction.'

I realise he is quirkier than he seems.

He fails to show up for our second date. We arrange to meet at a bar near Carnaby Street, but when I get off the Tube at Oxford Circus there's a text saying the Jubilee line's down and he can't get into town from Canary Wharf. Surely there must be another way to get here if he really wanted to? Was it cold feet?

In fact, he tells me when we meet up the following week it was gridlocked traffic. In the bar on Kingly Street, over *caipirinhas*, I decide he has the most beautiful blue eyes I've ever seen. Tonight, they are very smiley.

'You're very attractive,' he says during dinner in a Japanese restaurant on the same street. By the end of our date, I am longing for him to kiss me.

'Shall we go for a drink?' I suggest on our third date, after seeing Colin Firth in *A Single Man* at the Odeon on Shaftesbury Avenue. We are just across the road from Freud, a basement bar I went to a lot in my twenties. I decide its atmospheric concrete interior would be the perfect place to snog him in.

'No, I need to get back.' I assume he's not interested.

But the following morning, I receive a text. *Would you like to come over for dinner one night next week? x*

We arrange it for Tuesday. Over the weekend, I buy a short black dress from Zara. The Sunday is Valentine's Day and for once I am not in the least bothered to be alone.

He calls me on Monday night.

'I'm really sorry, but I'm going to have to cancel tomorrow. My ex-girlfriend got back in touch this weekend. And we've decided to give things another go.'

My effervescent mood dissolves.

'I could have seen us getting on really well together,' he says. It's the first time we've spoken on the phone and I realise how much I like his voice, with its hint of a northern accent. Hearing his words makes me sad, as I too had the sense we could have got on really well.

What appalling timing. How dare she choose that weekend! Will I ever meet the right person?

A couple of weeks later, I'm in a café with a friend on a Saturday morning. My phone bleeps. It's Mark.

How are you doing? When are you off to Bali?

I'm heading to Bali for a month to do another yoga teacher training.

I could ignore Mark. Is he playing me off against his ex, or confused about what he wants? But I decide to answer him. His response pings back immediately.

Are you free next Saturday? I have tickets for Romeo & Juliet at the Royal Opera House.

At the very least, it'll be a free trip to the Opera House.

I wear a short blue dress and much higher heels than usual. We don't speak about what happened since the previous time we met. We smuggle glasses of champagne into the box he has booked, hiding them under his sweater and giggling.

After the performance, we walk back to the Tube along the cobbles of Floral Street and, unused to my heels, I falter and almost come toppling over. He takes hold of my hand. And keeps holding it all the way to Leicester Square, and all the way down the escalator to the Northern Line. At the platform, we say goodbye. He is heading south to Kennington and I'm heading north to Chalk Farm. His lips touch mine, briefly.

'Can I see you again before you leave for Bali?' he asks.

Do you want to live dangerously and come over to my house & experience my cooking? he texts the day before we are due to meet.

I try not to let myself get too excited this time. What if he cancels again?

He lives in a two-storey cottage on a square in Kennington. My new Zara dress is much too thin for the cold early March night. He makes a fish pie, which is pretty good, even though he claims not to be very talented in the cooking department.

'You know I find you very attractive,' he says as we sit on the sofa after dinner, a polite distance between us.

'Are you actually single, though?'

'Yes. Totally. I wouldn't have got back in touch if I wasn't.'

We start kissing.

I fly to Bali thirty-six hours later. I spend the next four weeks living in a cottage set among lush green rice fields outside the town of Ubud. We study hard, beginning at seven in the morning and finishing at nine at night. I tell no one, not even my good friend Veronika with whom I'm sharing the cottage, about my fledging romance. But I think about Mark all the time. And in-between sessions on meditation and yoga philosophy, I check my phone for texts. But my old Nokia has suddenly decided to be completely unpredictable about when it receives incoming texts. Sometimes I'll message Mark and get no response for a couple of days. I fret that his ex might have persuaded him to give it yet another go. When a reply eventually arrives, I can see it was actually sent only minutes after I texted him. So much for modern technology.

I return to London in early April. Mark comes over to my flat the day after I get back. 'I missed you,' he says, as we lie in bed together on a rainy Tuesday afternoon.

He never asks about my surgery scar. I'm actually not particularly self-conscious about it these days. It's just become part of the landscape of my body, a body in which I feel quite at ease. But as through April and May we start spending increasing amounts of time together, it feels wrong not to tell him.

'Have you noticed the scar on my left breast?' I ask one night before we go to sleep.

'I hadn't.'

'I had breast cancer several years ago.'

He wraps his arms around me. 'No way, babe. I'm so sorry - that must have been tough.'

'It was.' I curl into his warmth, feel his heart beat against my chest. 'But I've been fine since.'

'Thank God.' He draws me even closer. 'I'm so lucky I found you.'

I hesitate. Now we're on the subject, should I bring up the additional part of the story? The one I often try and put out of my mind so I can pretend it isn't happening? I don't want to hide important things from him, I decide.

'Can I share something else with you?'

'Of course. I like learning all your different layers.'

'Last year one of my first cousins on my dad's side - she lives in Brazil and we've never actually met - got diagnosed with breast cancer. She's only in her mid-forties. Then she found out she has a mutated gene - it puts you at really high risk of it. And my doctors say the odds are I also have the gene. Though I haven't been able to face getting tested yet.'

'If you do, how likely is it you could get it again?'

'Up to eighty percent, apparently - over my lifetime. Which is a bit rubbish.'

Assuming I do have the gene, I could have a preventative double mastectomy and reconstruction. But I can't even bear to think about any of this yet. I've been clear of cancer for eight years and thought I could draw this chapter of my life to a close. The news of my cousin's cancer and this potential genetic mutation makes the ground beneath me feel far shakier. I find myself constantly feeling my breasts, almost expecting to find something there.

There's also the matter of my ovaries. The gene would put me at a thirty to forty percent lifetime risk of ovarian cancer, so it's recommended to ideally have your ovaries and fallopian tubes removed once you've completed your family, or by your early forties. But I am close to forty and have not yet had a child, although I still hope to. Mark and I have not discussed this yet. It feels too early in the relationship, which I just want to enjoy for now, having not had one for so long.

At the suggestion of Dr Jones, I've started to have an annual MRI scan, along with the ultrasound and mammogram I still have. MRIs are supposed to be much better at picking up tumours in women who do have the mutation. She also recommends a CA125 blood test every four months to monitor my ovaries. Although she warns me it's not yet been proven this test will ensure an early diagnosis of ovarian cancer, where it has high survival rates. Trials are still being carried out.

Irrationally, I am less anxious about getting ovarian cancer than I am about breast cancer, as no-one in my family has ever had it. Despite the fact that ovarian cancer is the one that's more likely to be diagnosed at late stage, by which time it usually has a poor prognosis.

I had my first breast MRI last autumn, just before I found Mark. No one warned me how claustrophobic it would feel. You lie face down on a bed attached to the machine, arms strapped by your sides. When the nurse started to slide me into the scanner's interior, its ceiling just a few centimetres above my head, I said, 'Take me back out. I don't think I can go through with this.' It took several attempts and a lot of pep-talking from the nurse to get me fully in. Once I was in, I tried taking slow deep breaths to calm me, but the radiographer's voice cut through my headphones.

'Please stop breathing like that. It's making you move too much and our images won't be clear enough.' The half hour I was trapped in there, bombarded by the machine's full range of rattling and bleeping and banging sounds, felt endless.

I, who almost never take medication, decided that next time I'd be accompanied by Valium. I've never suffered from claustrophobia before but since that scan, I feel panicky on Tube trains that stop in tunnels for more than a minute.

A few weeks after telling Mark I'd had cancer, I go for a routine breast ultrasound. The radiographer keeps coming back to one particular spot on my right breast. My body goes cold.

'Is everything ok?' I ask him.

'There's a small lump here. It's probably just a fibroadenoma.' I heard almost those exact words back in 2002. Then, I wasn't worried. Today, the word *probably* terrifies me.

'I'll need to do a needle biopsy on it, to be sure.'

He smears local anaesthetic on my breast to numb it and plunges the needle in.

'On a scale of one to ten, how concerned are you?'

'About three.'

Three! Which means a thirty percent chance of it being cancer.

'How soon can you get the results back?'

'Hopefully tomorrow afternoon. If not, it'll be Monday.'

I call Mark. He's in Paris for work today. We weren't meant to be seeing one another tonight - we quite often don't on weekdays as he has to be up at five-thirty each morning.

'I'm coming straight over from St Pancras.'

When he arrives, we lie on my sofa together.

'I'm really scared.' I'm unable to be rational and realise that the radiographer said there was a seven out of ten chance it was nothing. All I can think about was how I was misdiagnosed last time. *It's definitely not cancer,* my surgeon said in 2002, minutes before I was taken down to theatre.

'While I was on the train home,' Mark says, 'I decided that whatever happens, I'm sticking around. I'm falling in love with you.'

We hold one another tightly. The possibility of this intense happiness I've experienced over the past two months being shattered is unbearable.

The following day is a Friday and I have three yoga classes to teach. Since the start of the year I've been doing less architecture and more yoga. The recession is in full swing and I haven't been receiving many architecture enquiries recently, but I have got a lot of new yoga classes.

A good thing about teaching is it forces me to be totally focused, to be present for my students, to listen to the words I'm saying, concentrate on the poses I'm offering. But as soon as I finish a class, I grab my phone to see if there's been a call from the surgeon's office. Each time there's nothing. At the end of the day, I phone them and am told I'll have to wait until Monday.

Mark and I spend the weekend distracting ourselves. We go to a dance performance at the Barbican set to music by David Bowie and Lou Reed, we take a picnic to Primrose Hill. The weather is beautiful, just like it was that May weekend eight years ago when I waited to find out what was going on.

When Monday comes around I am terrified again, constantly checking my phone when I'm not teaching. Despite all the meditation and yoga I've done over the years, I find it hard to dispel the deep-seated fear of getting sick again that this has triggered.

Towards the end of the day, when I'm back home, the breast unit's number appears on my phone screen. I hesitate before I picking up. The secretary's voice is neutral as she asks to speak to me. It is impossible to predict what she is about to say.

'It's come back clear. Everything's completely normal.'

I put the phone down and burst into tears.

Mark is away for work again, but my parents and I celebrate by going out for a curry.

Later that month, I learn that another first cousin, also on my father's side, has been diagnosed with breast cancer. And that my cousin in Brazil now has secondary breast cancer. It seems almost inevitable that I carry this mutated gene. If only I'd known years ago. Then I could have told my cousins and they could have had the right check-ups or surgery and might never have got sick, or at least probably been diagnosed with an early stage cancer.

The irony is that my mother was tested for a *BRCA* mutation the year after I got sick. When the doctors found out that she was of Ashkenazi Jewish origin, they recommended it, as *BRCA* mutations are higher among Ashkenazis. She was negative, and it never crossed anyone's mind that it might have come through my non-Jewish father's side of the family.

Despite knowing what I know, I am still sometimes in denial that my illness could have been anything other than random chance. I feel like I have done my time with this disease and don't want to be dealing with its shadow anymore.

In September, my cousin from Brazil dies, leaving behind her husband, her father and her brother and sister. It hits me again how incredibly lucky I was that my cancer was picked up early enough to give me a chance.

In October, I finally visit a genetics consultant at The Royal Marsden. Professor Eeles tells me I have a ninety-eight percent chance of carrying the *BRCA1* mutation.

'But I can see you're not emotionally ready to have the test yet. There's a huge difference between thinking you might have it, and knowing for certain that you do. Until you're ready, the best thing you can do is to keep being screened at high level.'

I am relieved she hasn't insisted on an immediate mastectomy and removal of my ovaries, as I feared she might. I'm still only just starting to digest this latest twist to my story and can't yet face doing what sounds so radical. And while a part of me is scared of getting a new cancer, another part tells me that I've been fine for eight years, so there's every chance I can carry on being so for a while longer.

In November, Mark tells me he has been headhunted to be head of commodities analysis for an energy company in Dusseldorf.

'I don't know what to do,' he says. 'It's a great job, but I'm worried it could affect us. It'll probably be for a couple of years.'

I know he hasn't been happy at work for a while, and that given there's a recession in the UK, new jobs are not so easy to come by. Much as I don't want him to go away, I don't want him to stay here and be miserable either.

We discuss my joining him there, but both agree it wouldn't be ideal. Given how minimal my German is, it'd be hard for me to work as a yoga teacher or an architect. And neither of us think it'd wise for me to join in him a fairly unexciting city in which I have no job and he's the only person I know. We agree he'll take the job and we'll make sure we see one another at least every other weekend.

Our long-distance relationship begins in the spring of 2011. Usually he travels back to London, although occasionally we meet in other cities, such as Berlin or Paris. Once in a while I visit him in Dusseldorf, although we both decide London is a lot more fun.

It's always exciting seeing him again after almost two weeks apart. But the downside is that late on Sunday afternoon, once I have become so used to having him around me again, he has to leave. I always spend the next couple of days feeling out of sorts as I readjust to life by myself.

We talk about marriage and children. I am keen to marry, he is more cautious, having been through a divorce.

'I know I want to always be with you, but I just don't know if I want to get married again,' he says.

We agree we want to try for a child, although we realise being forty, it might not happen, especially as we live in different countries.

I have a blood test to check my fertility.

'Your hormones levels are good for someone your age,' the doctor tells me.

'Despite the chemotherapy?'

'Yes. They're still above average. You were very young when you had it, so more often than not the body rebalances itself.'

By the end of 2013, when we have been together almost four years and he is still living in Dusseldorf, I have almost given up hope of us marrying. We have a very loving and committed relationship so I decide to be grateful for that rather than getting obsessed about becoming his wife.

When he invites me away for a surprise weekend over Valentine's Day in 2014, I assume it's just that, even though a couple of friends text me before I leave to say, *You have to let me know if anything happens!*

We meet in Munich where he tells me that the following day we're going to a spa hotel a couple of hours south of the city. It's at an old castle in the mountains and I once told Mark in passing that I dreamt about visiting it.

In the morning, before our train leaves, we wander round Munich's *Altestadt*. On the *Marienplatz*, the square with the town hall on it, an American man gets down on one knee and surprises his girlfriend with a huge diamond ring.

'What would you do if I proposed to you?' I ask Mark.

'I'd probably say yes.' This surprises me.

But I don't. Partly because we are hungry and in a rush to make it back to the delicious restaurant we discovered yesterday with the best chocolate mousse ever, where we'll have lunch before our train leaves for the spa. And mostly because, old fashioned as it sounds, I'd still quite like him to do the asking.

We stand on the balcony of our room at the hotel, admiring the view across snow-capped mountains. We've just arrived and I am desperate for the loo. But before I have a chance to go, Mark says, 'I haven't brought you here just because it's Valentine's Day. I wanted to ask you to marry me.'

'Are you serious? Only a few weeks ago you told me you might never be ready!'

'That was so you wouldn't guess. I've been planning this for months! Are you going to say yes, then?'

A couple of weeks after we return from Germany, and just as we are starting to plan our wedding, I receive the results of the

BRCA gene test I finally took at the end of 2013. Of course, a part of me hopes I'll be one of the lucky two percent who despite our family history do not carry the mutation.

A phone call from The Royal Marsden Hospital confirms that I am not one of the lucky ones. I do indeed have the *BRCA1* mutation. Even though the news shouldn't have been a surprise, I sit on my sofa, shaken.

But actually, I *am* one of the lucky ones. Both my cousins are now dead. Twelve years after my diagnosis, I am well and able to make choices; choices that it was too late for my cousins to make.

Our wedding is in early September. It rains in the morning, which is supposed to be good luck. In the afternoon, while I am getting ready, the sun comes out and offers us a perfect late summer day.

We marry at St George's on Hanover Square, surrounded by ninety of our nearest and dearest. It is the same church where I had a vision of my funeral taking place, twelve springs ago, during a Good Friday performance of the *St Matthew* Passion.

I wear a pale grey long silk dress and I walk in to church on my father's arm to Bach's Arioso, played by my sister on the violin. After the ceremony, several people tell me it made them cry.

Had someone said to me, the day I was diagnosed, that all these years later I'd be back in that church marrying this man, I doubt I would have believed them.

Mark and I lead our guests through the streets of Soho to our reception at the Union Club, an atmospheric members' club in a townhouse on Greek Street, where we eat and drink and dance until the early hours. It is without a doubt the best day of my life.

31

'My plastic surgeon tells me you need to eat more cake,' says Mr Gui, my consultant at The Royal Marsden.

It is the first time I've been told I'm too skinny for something. In this case, having my breasts reconstructed using tissue from my own body. Unless I am willing to go down a cup size or two. Which is not an option. I am only a B, and if I'm going to go through with this surgery, I want to end up with breasts that are at least the same size, hopefully a little bigger. The 'boob job' is what Mark and I call it. Mastectomy is too ugly a word.

I deliberate over breast surgery for two years after learning I am *BRCA1* positive. I veer between thinking I am mad to chop off a still healthy part of my body that might never be diseased again, and that I am mad not to. Won't my healthy lifestyle of daily yoga and meditation, a mostly organic diet full of cancer-busting fruit and vegetables, turmeric and a few other supplements, plus almost no alcohol protect me? Some days these feel like fortress walls, others, paper thin screens. Part of me is brazen, trusting I'll be fine. Another part is fearful, thinking my body did this once, so why not again? After all, at the time of my diagnosis, I was already slim, ate healthily and exercised. Yet I still managed to get the disease very young, even for a *BRCA* carrier. And what if next time it was caught too late?

Over the years, doctors have given varying statistics, ranging from a fifty to an eighty-five percent chance of the risk of being diagnosed with a new breast cancer over my lifetime. These doctors do agree that if cancer were found, it would probably be caught early, thanks to my high-level screening, and therefore likely to be curable.

'Curable' might well, nonetheless, include another run-in with chemo, and of course navigating the intense and prolonged fear that inevitably accompanies a cancer diagnosis. Most of the time, I glibly focus on the word 'curable,' blocking out my memories, which are too uncomfortable to revisit. My family, however, are concerned, and l know they long for me to have surgery.

Three things help me make my decision. I read a memoir by Jessica Queller, a thirty-something New Yorker, who works in film. She and her equally glamourous sister are *BRCA1* carriers. Both opted for risk-reducing surgery. Despite similar anxieties to mine, over how their new breasts would look and feel, they are both thrilled with the results. If they can do it, so can I, I tell myself. Then I have a particularly challenging experience at an MRI scan, and despite the Valium almost don't make it into the tunnel. And I realise I'm done with them, and with the sitting outside the surgeon's office waiting for results, fearful that this time my luck will have run out and I'll fall on the wrong side of the line

Finally, I hear of an acquaintance of a friend, diagnosed with Stage 1 breast cancer, who died of secondaries just a couple of years later. It is a wake-up call that even early diagnosis is not a sure-fire guarantee of a cure.

I am still, however, not quite ready to let go of my ovaries.

'Around one to two in a hundred *BRCA1* carriers like you will be diagnosed with cancer for each year you leave it,' Professor Eeles at The Royal Marsden tells me.

It's not an easy choice to make. I'm fully aware I'm taking a small risk by keeping my ovaries for a little longer, and in a way that might seem like madness. On the other hand, I instinctively feel I need to be at a place where I've fully explored trying to have a baby before I have them removed.

We have tried a couple of rounds of natural cycle *IVF*, using no drugs, as my doctors have advised me against taking any hormones while I still have my own breasts as they would increase my risk of breast cancer. But once I've had my mastectomy, I can try *IVF* with medication.

My new breasts will be silicon. My own tissue will be removed and the implants put in during just one operation. I have my pre-surgery appointment a few days after Donald Trump wins the election. Boob-jobs are now a major topic of conversation between Mark and me. He moved back to London a year ago, just after our first wedding anniversary, so we are finally, for the first time, living together. One night after supper, we Google Melania Trump's topless photos.

'She looks pretty good,' we agree.

'Why don't you take a photo to the hospital and say that's what you want?' he suggests.

'You must be bloody joking if you think I'm walking into The Royal Marsden with a naked photo of Melania. Anyway, you know they've recommended I only go a bit bigger.'

The hospital insist I see before and after photos of other women who've had the same surgery. They've told me not to expect too much, so I don't risk disappointment. Some of the women look even better than before. I can only pray I'll be one of them.

My surgery is booked for Tuesday 6 December. The Saturday before, Mark surprises me with a carefully planned day out: breakfast at a café in Fitzrovia, a massage, dinner at our favourite restaurant, The Palomar, and a performance of *Mamma Mia*.

I realise I am finally ready for this. I have a fantastic surgeon. I've done enough research to learn that it is indeed possible to be satisfied, delighted even, with the results. And somehow I have a deep-seated trust that all will be well.

On the day, I'm surprised by how calm I feel.

I only wobble when I'm in pre-theatre. The operation before mine has overrun, so I'm kept waiting ages. It gives me too much time to think, and on the cusp, I falter. Once I go in, I can never go back. But right now, I could still get up and leave.

'Perhaps I'm making a huge mistake,' I tell the nurse. Will I come round from the anaesthetic in tears, full of regrets?

'When we spoke earlier, you were certain. And it was clearly not a decision you'd made lightly.'

When I wake, the calmness is still there. My only anxiety is whether they've saved my nipples, as there was a small chance they could have been destroyed during the surgery. Thankfully, they are still with me.

The pain is unremarkable. I am sick several times from the anaesthetic, but then I always am.

I leave the hospital exactly twenty-four hours after I arrived. I am accompanied by two cumbersome plastic drain bottles, whose lengths of clear plastic tubing hang off my waist. Reddish brown fluid from the surgery sites drips slowly down the tubes and sloshes around in the bottles.

Two days later, my new companions hidden under an oversized coat belonging to Mark, I make it out of the flat to visit my acupuncturist.

Ross checks my pulses. 'I've never seen someone so un-traumatised by surgery. Even people coming in after having wisdom teeth out are in more of a state of shock. I think this has been really cathartic for you.'

Later, I walk down Marylebone High Street. I spent a lot of time on this street in my Chemo Days, as I call them, because it was round the corner from the oncology unit. I recall another Friday lunchtime on this same street, fourteen years ago, a chilly October day, when I was about to have what I hoped would be my last ever session of chemo. Today is a sunny, mild December day. A busker plays the sax, a horse-drawn carriage ambles past. I am euphoric to still be walking this street, so many years later. I spend over two hours in Le Pain Quotidien, having lunch and laughing and chatting with Anat. It's only when I get home, I realise I may have overdone it.

The following day, I wake up grumpy. The drains are pulling on my skin, and I almost tripped over one of them when I got up to go to the loo in the night. They are still collecting too much fluid per day to be removed. Even though I've been told they typically come out seven to ten days after surgery, and it's only been four so far, I am impatient.

I hear of the writer AA Gill's death, just three weeks after announcing he had *the full English of cancers*. It puts my drains into perspective.

They come out six days after surgery. By then, I'm off the painkillers, too. Hoisting myself out of bed is the only time I feel any serious discomfort. The worst side effect of the surgery is not being able to sleep properly: for the first two weeks, I am only allowed on my back. I don't manage more than an hour at a time. And in the middle of each night, wide awake, I drag myself to the sofa, where I read for hours, before finally drifting off, usually just as Mark is getting up for work.

Life, in these immediate post-surgery days, takes on a new rhythm, one which, sleep deprivation aside, I enjoy. In the mornings I take a walk, often through Regent's Park or Primrose Hill. I sit in cafes drinking tea and reading novels, more often than not enjoying something delicious like a croissant or a scone.

I intended to eat healthily, as I wanted to heal as fast as possible. But I can't even look at the kale and wild salmon sitting in the fridge. What my body wants, in these tender post-surgery days, is comfort food: buttered white toast; spinach and ricotta tortelloni; a baked potato with cottage cheese. Exactly the things I craved right after chemotherapy all those years ago.

Afternoons are spent back on the sofa, reading and trying to catch up on the sleep I'm not getting at night. And as Christmas is approaching, in the evenings there are parties to go to.

For a short time, I acquire an Uber and a blow-dry habit. I could probably just about wash my hair myself, but decide it's a good excuse to get the salon sleek hair I love. I turn up to parties with my new silicon breasts (still clad in their hospital dressings) and glossy hair and people tell me how well I look. I have only told my family and a few close friends about the surgery. Most people don't have a clue.

After a week of going out most nights, I am exhausted. My inability to sleep properly is really catching up with me.

'You're doing too much,' Mark tells me. 'Cut yourself some slack. You had a major operation barely a week ago.'

At first, I resist. I want to taste life fully, and make the most of my month off work and all these free evenings, when I'd usually be teaching yoga. Since having the cancer, I've often felt like I must seize every moment. It awakened in me the realisation we never know quite how much time we have left.

Eventually, I give in to the exhaustion, cancel all my arrangements for the next few days, pretending I, like much of London, have the flu.

Ten days after surgery, I return to The Royal Marsden to have my dressings removed. I will see my new breasts properly for the first time. What if I hate them?

I walk over to the mirror. My skin is still yellow with bruising. But, even so, they look great. A little bigger. A lot more uplift. And perfectly symmetrical.

Ana, a Spanish doctor I've not met before, is called in to inspect them. 'You could go on the beach today, in a tiny bikini,' she says, 'and no one would guess a thing.'

'Wow, they look like a sixteen-year old's,' says my friend Ayala a couple of days later, when she comes over for tea.

'Much better than before,' declares my mother, direct as ever.

Mark is delighted, too.

Six weeks after my operation, I fly to Goa for a yoga retreat. It's a trip I almost certainly wouldn't have taken had it not been for the surgery. Money from an unexpected architecture project has also helped facilitate it. It feels like the perfect opportunity to mark the end of this journey.

I anticipated having to miss out a lot of the poses, especially ones that use the upper body. To my surprise, soon I am doing headstands and handstands again. I go on the beach in a bikini, utterly unselfconscious. Just deeply grateful to be here, and to have been given a second chance, something too many others have been denied.

My new breasts have limited sensation. While certain areas of the skin feel almost unchanged, at least half of each breast registers touch in only the most subtle of ways. It is not the complete numbness that the doctors warned me might happen, and it bothers me less than I thought it would. While it can be strange to touch a part of your body that was once so receptive and feel so little, with that also comes the reassurance that this is now a much safer territory.

Most of the time, I forget I even have implants. If anything, I feel even more feminine since the surgery. While I didn't dislike my original breasts, I am prouder of this pair. Not so much because of what they look like, but for the story behind them.

THREE

32

I am back in hospital.

It's the first time I've been conscious in an operating theatre. Mark is with me. He wears blue scrubs and his hair is covered by a pale blue mesh cap.

'Have you got your playlist ready?' the doctor asks.

It's a playlist I built over the last few weeks. I envisaged hearing it in a dimly-lit lavender-scented room. It includes some of my favourite Christmas carols, such as 'In the Bleak Midwinter', and music we had at our wedding like John Rutter's 'The Lord Bless you and Keep You'. During the ceremony, as the choir sang this prayer, I felt the music wrap a protective blanket around me. It *will* still happen, it seemed to be telling me.

Mark puts on Snow Patrol's 'Chasing Cars'. The doctor starts singing along... *We'll do it all...*

'Really good choice,' he says in his Irish accent. 'I saw them once in concert, you know.'

When I walked into the anaesthetic-room, I assumed I'd be unfazed by the preparations. It's not as if I'm unfamiliar with surgery. But this is very different to being put out by a general. The anaesthetist sat me up on the bed and prodded my lower back, trying to find the right spot for the needle. My body tightened.

I wanted to breathe him into the world. To ride the waves of sensation, as all these years of yoga have taught me. But my due date was yesterday and I am over forty. The advice, at this age, is not to go beyond it.

Over the past couple of weeks, I drank raspberry leaf tea every-day, had acupuncture twice, walked everywhere, took nightly Epsom salt baths. But the baby floated happily in my body, his head yet to engage with my cervix.

I chose to have a Caesarean over being induced because most of my friends who were induced - particularly those over forty - ended up having emergency C-sections, something I'm keen to avoid.

Even when I woke up this morning, I was hoping to go into labour. As Mark and I took a cab through pre-dawn London, Regent's Street illuminated by giant gold and silver angels, still I hoped. I kept hoping as we stood in the dark on Piccadilly, outside the arched stone entranceway of our favourite breakfast place, waiting for it to open.

Nothing to eat after 8am, the hospital instructed.

I ate pancakes with berries and drank two pots of Assam tea, no longer caring about moderating my caffeine intake. And even then, I hoped.

After breakfast, we walked the short distance to St George's Church and lit a candle. Almost instantly, its flame faded to a flicker.

'What if there's something wrong?' I asked Mark.

'Don't worry, my love. I'm sure he's fine.' He put his arm around me, as always my grounding force.

By the time we returned home it was raining. In just two hours we had to be at the hospital. Still no signs. I cried a little, knowing it was now time to let go of this particular dream.

'You're really tense,' says the anaesthetist as he prods. 'Let's give you a gin & tonic.'

'A gin & tonic!?' I say, as Mark laughs at my gullibility.

'No, not really! Really, it's a mix of valium and morphine to get you nice and relaxed.'

I am calm, distant even. A green canvas screen has been placed above my ribcage, and I can neither see nor feel what's going on beyond it.

'We're almost there,' says the doctor.

I'm surprised by how fast it's happening. '

'You should get whatever song you want for the big moment on,' he tells Mark.

It was an easy choice: 'Viva la Vida' by Coldplay. We played it for our first dance at our wedding. A song that makes us both want to jump up and down with joy.

The green screen is lowered. On the darkest day of the year, one hour before sunset, Alexander Isambard is lifted out of the safe embrace of my body and greeted by the bright lights of the theatre.

Finally, we meet skin to skin. After all these months, I can feel his heartbeat, his shallow breath.

I am content as I hold him, but it's not the overwhelming experience I'd anticipated. Perhaps the drugs have muted me?

Alexander is bigger than my scans predicted. 'He'll be about seven pounds,' the radiographer said at my last one, when I was thirty-six weeks.

He is over nine pounds and has a large head.

'You're lucky you didn't try and do it naturally,' the doctor says. 'I think you'd have had a hard time of it. It all worked out for the best in the end.'

Sometimes, things do work out for the best. But not always.

While I was pregnant, I envisaged writing the ending to this book. The fairy-tale one: girl survives cancer, eventually meets the love of her life, and even has a baby.

The reality is, life can catch you off guard, just as it did on that May day back in 2002.

Last week, it did again.

Nine days ago, my sister, Tanya, died. Suddenly. Her story is complicated. It's not for now, though.

Shock. The desire to protect my baby. These got me through the past nine days.

I tune out most of the world. I've even taken a step back from my parents, as I don't want to be near their grief. I distract myself by finally packing my hospital bag, by unwrapping and washing tiny white sleepsuits, by reading, losing myself in Michelle Obama's memoir.

I'd loved the final few weeks of pregnancy; a threshold space, where work paused and motherhood had yet to begin. A world of café breakfasts with friends, naps on wintry afternoons, early evening movies, of cooking.

Suddenly, I am desperate for Alexander to arrive.

Despite the huge loss of Tanya, I am taken aback by the beauty in the world. It's there as I walk through a stark Primrose Hill, listening to the *St Matthew* Passion, my cheeks embracing the aliveness of cold air. It's there in the kindness of others: my acupuncturist comes in just to see me, even though he'd cancelled all his other appointments to look after his wife and children who were sick. And Paola won't leave my side that day, waiting outside the acupuncturist's room, accompanying me to my haircut, to John Lewis to buy a steriliser.

While there's a determination in me to savour life, I'm also edgy. I place an online order for feeding bottles and when my credit card is declined, I slam my fist on the table and scream, 'Fuck you.' I accidentally drop the hazelnuts I've toasted for a pasta dish on the floor as I take them out of the oven, and start crying.

One evening, I can't get hold of Mum. She's not answering her phone. I start sobbing hysterically. What if she's gone, too?

'Sorry, I accidentally left my mobile in the car when I went out,' she tells Mark who keeps trying her number, as I'm now too beside myself pick up the phone.

The night before my due date, when we should have been celebrating my sister's birthday, we all go for a curry in Belsize Park. Josh, Tanya's ten-year-old son, wanted to do something in honour of her. I'm reluctant to go, preferring to stay with Mark in the protective bubble of our flat. But once I'm there, I'm grateful to be with my family.

Tanya's Godmother, who counts as family, raises a toast to Alexander's aunt.

'Thank you,' is my initial reaction, so used to being the only aunt in the family.

'It's a great honour to be an aunt,' my sister said to me the last time I saw her, eighteen days before her death.

The day after Alexander's birth is when I fall in love. I cuddle our miracle baby, conceived on what we agreed would be a final round of *IVF*. I stroke the softness of his almost hairless scalp, and it's fierce, this feeling that rises up inside. It scares me. For accompanying it is the fear of losing him. And there's the knowledge that one day - hopefully in the very distant future but, nonetheless, one day - we will have to say goodbye to one another.

I hold Alexander and I also long for my sister. I want to wrap my arms around her. I always loved hugging her; the smell of her hair, her skin gave me a sense of homecoming. A familiarity Alexander and I still need to learn with one another.

We leave the hospital on Christmas Eve. The cab driver takes a left on Albany Street. Ahead of us is Regent's Park. Beyond the black of its railings, its bare trees, the sky blazes orange as the day takes its final breaths. Next to me, nestled in his car-seat, my beautiful son dozes, oblivious to this dance of dark and light.

There is no such thing as Happy Ever After. But there are perfect moments, jewels scattered amidst the wild unpredictability of life, even hidden within crevasses of despair. All we can do is seek them out. And when we find them, to hold them close, so very close.

Acknowledgments

I am deeply grateful to my first readers - the current members of ReWord and former members of The Clink Street Writers - for their support, encouragement and invaluable feedback. In particular, I'd like to thank Michelle Lovric, Paola de Carolis, Pamela Johnson and Jane Kirwan for generously reading the entire manuscript, as did Mike Shaw, Lucy Edge and Francis Gilbert.

Thanks too to Jill Foulston for her brilliant editing of the final manuscript, and to Mavis Gregson for her meticulous copy-editing. Any remaining mistakes are my own. Thanks to Alex Kirby for his beautiful cover design.

Thank you to my family, for their endless support and love through challenging times. Thank you to all my wonderful friends. They are too many to name, but they know who they are. A special note of thanks has to go to Paola de Carolis and Anat Talmor for being by my side every step of the way. And thank you to Mark Hives and Alexander Hives. During those dark days of illness, I could not have believed that such an incredible husband and son would one day come my way.

Thank you to my amazing oncologist, Alison Jones, not only for her medical brilliance, but for always believing in me. Professor Rosalind Eeles, my genetics consultant at The Royal Marsden, has been an ongoing source of incredible knowledge, as well as kindness. I am also so grateful to Gerald Gui, my fantastic surgeon at The Royal Marsden.

Thank you to the many people who helped me heal, and in particular to Chris Howe, who has become a lifelong friend.

I am also so grateful for the practice of yoga, which came into my life at just the right time, and provided invaluable support through my illness and beyond. I'm grateful to Triyoga, the studio I practiced at and am now lucky enough to teach at, for all their wonderful teachers, who helped me more than they could ever know.

Blue Door Press
bluedoorpress.co.uk

About

Annabel Chown was born in London and read Architecture at Cambridge University. She has worked as an architect in Berlin and London, and currently teaches yoga in London.

www.annabelchown.com

Printed in Great Britain
by Amazon

40756987R00173